AS Biology

There's a big jump from GCSE to AS Biology.
With so much new knowledge to get your head around,
you need to make sure you hit the ground running.

This book will give you a Head Start — it covers all those things that trip you up when you move from GCSE to AS, and includes loads of practice questions to make sure you've got the hang of it all.

Spend the first week of 6th form or (whisper it quietly) the summer holiday working through it so everything will make perfect sense when you start your AS.

We've done our bit — the rest is up to you.

What CGP is all about

Our sole aim here at CGP is to produce the highest quality books — carefully written, immaculately presented and dangerously close to being funny.

Then we work our socks off to get them out to you — at the cheapest possible prices.

Contents

Section One — Biological Molecules

Section Two — Cell Structure

Section Three — Genetics and Cell Division

Section Four — Diet and Digestion

Section Five — Disease and Immunity

Section Six — Exchange

Section Seven — The Circulatory System and Disease

Section Eight — Variation, Evolution and Classification

Section Nine — Plants

Section Ten — Investigating and Interpreting

Published by CGP

Author:
Barbara Green

Editors:
Ellen Bowness, Jane Towle

With thanks to Tom Cain for the proofreading.

ISBN: 978 1 84762 117 7

Groovy website: www.cgpbooks.co.uk
Jolly bits of clipart from CorelDRAW®
Printed by Elanders Ltd, Newcastle upon Tyne.

Based on the classic CGP style created by Richard Parsons.

Proteins

Proteins Are Made of Amino Acids

Proteins are composed of long chains of amino acids. There are twenty different amino acids used in proteins. They all contain carbon, hydrogen, oxygen and nitrogen, and some contain sulfur. All have the same structure as the one in the diagram but R can be one of twenty different chemical groups.

An amino acid

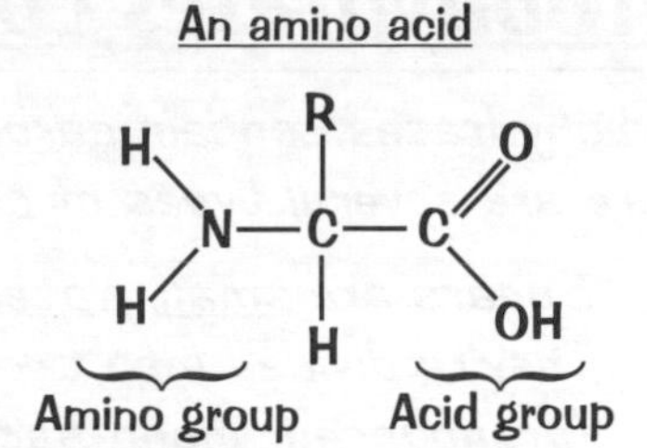

Proteins are Held Together by Covalent Bonds

1) The chains of amino acids are attached to each other by strong covalent bonds.
2) The amino acids can be arranged in any sequence and proteins can be up to several hundred amino acids long.
3) The number of different proteins that are possible is almost unimaginable. Consider that there are several thousand ways of arranging a chain of just three amino acids, with each combination forming a different protein. Add one more amino acid to the chain and the number of possibilities leaps into the hundreds of thousands.
4) It's the order of the amino acids in a protein that determines its structure and it's the structure of a protein that determines how it works.

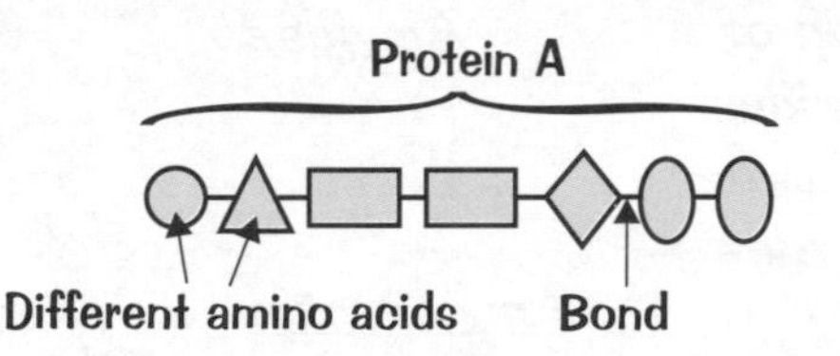

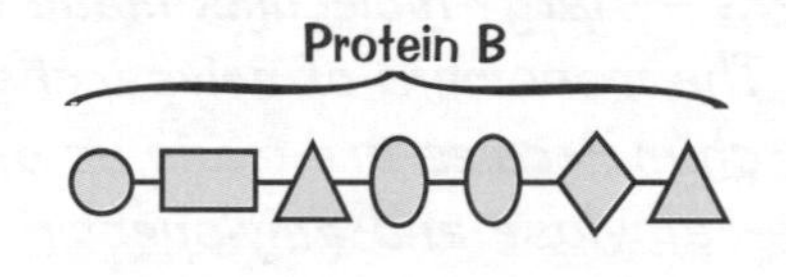

(N.B. Each different shape represents a different type of amino acid.)

Each Protein has its Own Special Shape

1) The order in which the amino acids are arranged in a protein chain is called the primary structure.
2) Some chains coil up or fold into pleats that are held together by weak forces of chemical attraction called hydrogen bonds. The coils and pleats are the secondary structure of a protein.
3) Some proteins (especially enzymes) have a tertiary structure. The coiled chain of amino acids is folded into a ball that's held together by a mixture of weak chemical bonds (e.g. hydrogen bonds) and stronger bonds (e.g. sulfur bridges).
4) If the protein has a roughly spherical shape it's called a globular protein (e.g. enzymes are classed as globular proteins).

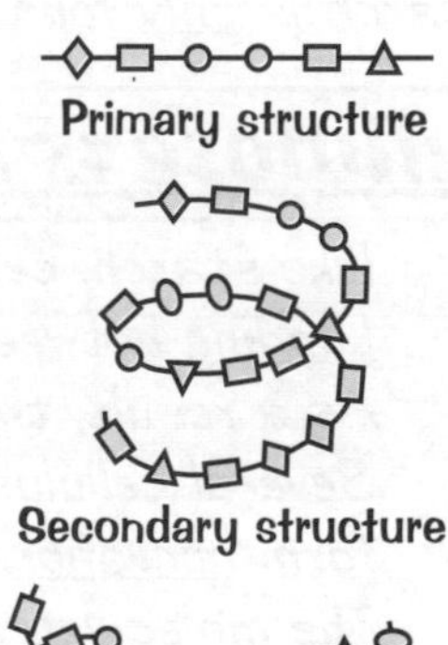

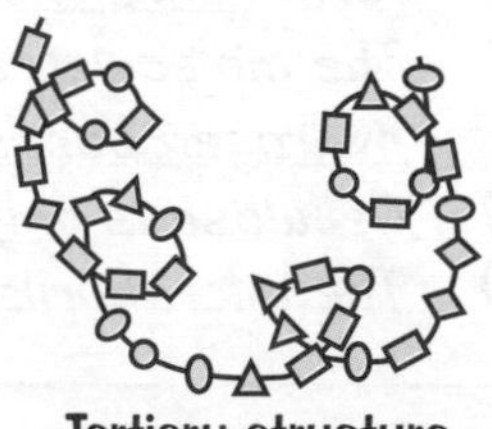

Test your understanding with the questions below:

1) What is the primary structure of a protein?
2) What type of bond holds together the secondary structure of a protein?

Answers

1) The order in which the amino acids are arranged in a chain.
2) Hydrogen bonds (weak forces of chemical attraction).

Carbohydrates

Carbohydrates Contain Three Elements

Carbohydrates contain <u>carbon</u>, <u>hydrogen</u> and <u>oxygen</u>.
There are several types of carbohydrate, e.g. sugars, starch and cellulose.

1) Sugars are <u>small</u>, <u>water-soluble</u> molecules that taste sweet.
2) They're divided into two groups: <u>monosaccharides</u> (pronounced: mono-sack-a-rides) and <u>disaccharides</u> (die-sack-a-rides).
3) Monosaccharides are the single units from which all the other carbohydrates are built. <u>Glucose</u> and <u>fructose</u> are both monosaccharides.
4) Disaccharides are formed when <u>two monosaccharides</u> are joined together by a chemical reaction. A molecule of <u>water</u> is also formed (so it's called a <u>condensation reaction</u>).

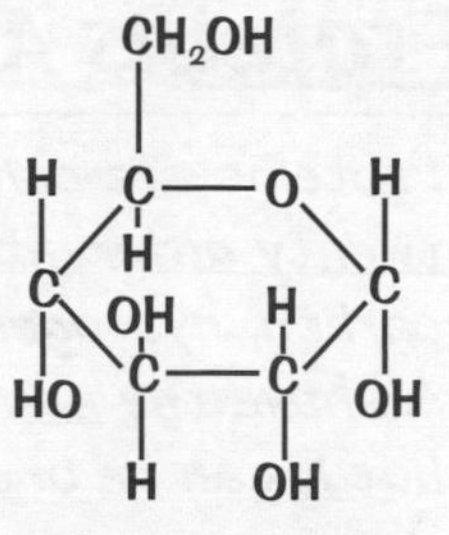

Structural formula of glucose ($C_6H_{12}O_6$)

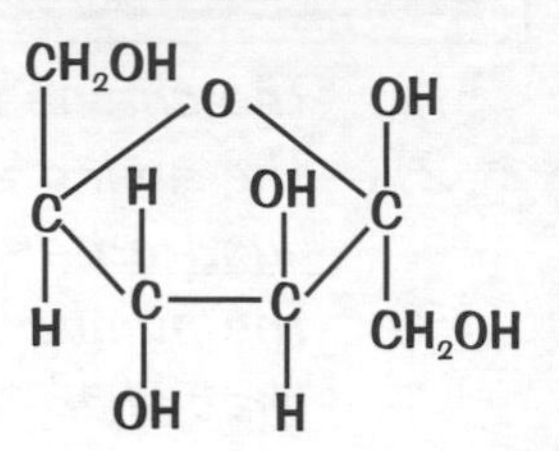

Structural formula of fructose ($C_6H_{12}O_6$)

GLUCOSE + GLUCOSE → MALTOSE (a disaccharide) + WATER
GLUCOSE + FRUCTOSE → SUCROSE (a disaccharide) + WATER

Starch is a Polysaccharide

<u>Polysaccharides</u> are <u>polymers</u> — large molecules made up of <u>monomers</u> (smaller units). The monomers of polysaccharides are <u>monosaccharides</u>. <u>Starch</u> molecules are made up of two different polysaccharides — <u>amylose</u> and <u>amylopectin</u>, which are polymers of glucose. The insoluble, compact starch molecules are an ideal way of <u>storing glucose</u>. Starch is <u>only</u> found in plant cells.

Amylose

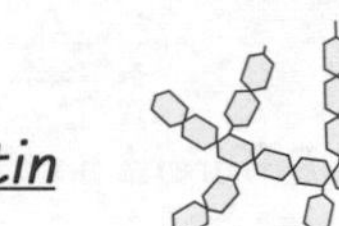

Amylopectin

Cellulose is Also a Polysaccharide

1) Like starch, cellulose is a polymer of glucose, but the <u>bonding</u> between the glucose units is different.
2) As a result, the cellulose molecules are <u>long</u> and <u>straight</u>.
3) Several cellulose molecules can lie side by side to form <u>microfibrils</u>.
4) The molecules are held together by many weak <u>hydrogen bonds</u>.
5) Cellulose is <u>only</u> found in plant cells.
6) The microfibrils <u>strengthen</u> the plant cell wall.

Three Cellulose molecules

etc.
etc.
etc.
Weak hydrogen bonds

Have a go at these questions:

1) Name two monosaccharides.
2) Which disaccharide is composed of two molecules of glucose?
3) Name two polysaccharides.

<u>Answers</u>

1) E.g. glucose and fructose.
2) Maltose.
3) E.g. starch and cellulose.

Lipids

Lipids Contain Carbon, Hydrogen and Oxygen

Lipids are oils and fats. Plant oils and animal fats are mostly made up of a group of lipids called triglycerides. A triglyceride consists of a molecule of glycerol with three fatty acids attached to it.

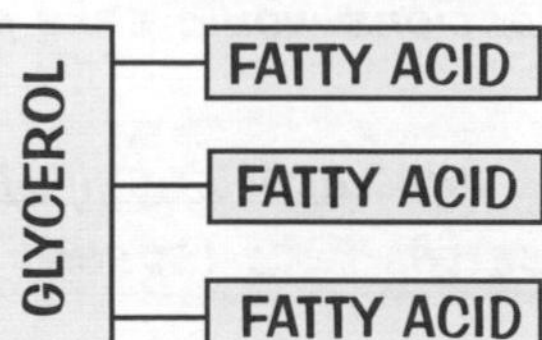

A triglyceride

A fatty acid molecule is a long chain of carbon atoms with an acid group (-COOH) at one end. Hydrogen atoms are attached to the carbon atoms. If every carbon atom in the chain is joined by a single bond, we say that the fatty acid is saturated. If one or more of the bonds is a double bond, it's said to be unsaturated. A fatty acid with many double bonds is polyunsaturated.

Saturated fatty acid

Unsaturated fatty acid

Phospholipids are a Special Type of Lipid

Phospholipids (pronounced: foss-foe-lip-id) are like triglycerides, but instead of having three fatty acid chains, they have two fatty acid chains and a phosphate group.
Cell membranes are made from a double layer of phospholipids.

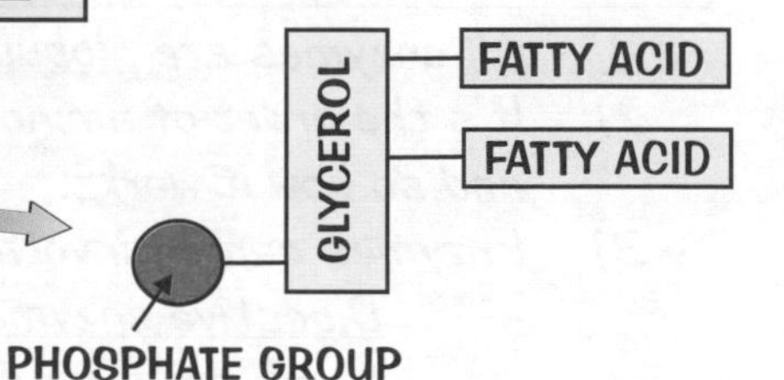

See if you can answer these questions:

1) Which element isn't present in lipids or carbohydrates but is always present in proteins?
2) What's the difference between saturated fatty acids and unsaturated fatty acids?
3) What's the difference between triglycerides and phospholipids?

Answers
1) Nitrogen.
2) Every carbon atom in saturated fatty acid chains is joined by a single bond.
Unsaturated fatty acids have one or more double bonds in their carbon chains.
3) Triglycerides have three fatty acid chains attached to a glycerol molecule. Phospholipids have two fatty acid chains and a phosphate group attached to a glycerol molecule.

Enzymes

Enzymes Help to Speed up Biochemical Reactions

In a living cell, thousands of biochemical reactions take place every second. The sum of these reactions is called metabolism. A single chain of biochemical reactions is called a metabolic pathway. Without enzymes, these reactions would take place very slowly at normal body temperature.

1) *Enzymes are biological catalysts.*
2) *They increase the rate (speed) of reactions.*

How do Enzymes Act as Catalysts?

1) *Even reactions that release energy require an input of energy to get them going, e.g. the gas from a Bunsen burner doesn't burn until you provide heat energy from a match.*
2) *This input energy is called the activation energy. A reaction that needs a high activation energy can't start at a low temperature of 37 °C (i.e. body temperature).*
3) *Enzymes reduce the activation energy.*

This graph shows the activation energies of a reaction with and without an enzyme:

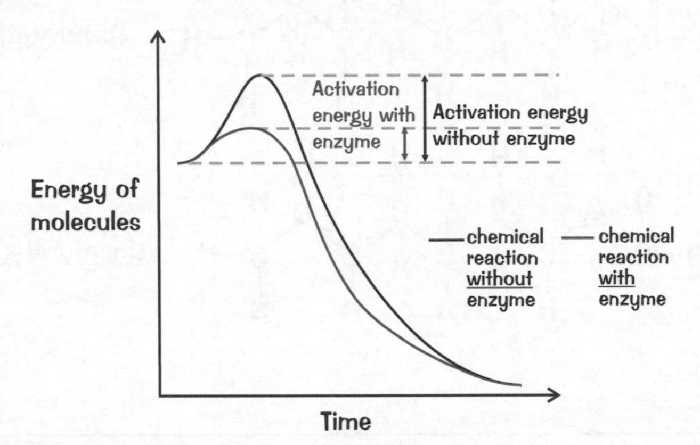

Enzymes are Proteins

1) *All enzymes are globular proteins (because they're roughly spherical).*
2) *It's the order of amino acids in an enzyme that determines its structure, and so how it works.*
3) *Enzymes can be involved in breaking down molecules or building molecules. For example:*
   - *Digestive enzymes are important in the digestive system, where they help to break down food into smaller molecules, e.g. carbohydrases break down carbohydrates.*
   - *Enzymes involved in DNA replication help to build molecules, e.g. DNA polymerase.*

Answer the quick quiz below:

1) *Where would you find a metabolic pathway: in a park, a cell, a field or alongside a main road? You may phone a friend or ask the audience.*
2) *What is activation energy?*
3) *What do digestive enzymes do?*

Answers

1) *In a cell.*
2) *Activation energy is the energy required to get a reaction started.*
3) *Break down food.*

Enzymes

Enzymes have an Active Site

1) A substance that's acted upon by an enzyme is called its <u>substrate</u>.
2) The <u>active site</u> is a region on the surface of the enzyme molecule where a substrate molecule can attach itself. It's where the catalysed reaction takes place.
3) The shape of the substrate molecule and the shape of the active site are <u>complementary</u>, i.e. they fit each other.
4) Almost as soon as the <u>enzyme-substrate complex</u> has formed, the products of the reaction are released and the enzyme is ready to accept another substrate molecule.

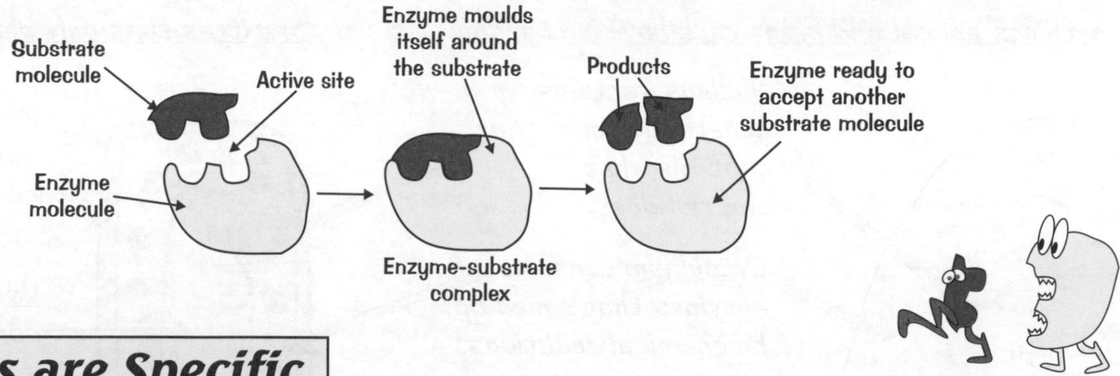

Enzymes are Specific

1) An enzyme usually catalyses one <u>specific</u> chemical reaction.
2) The substrate molecule must be the <u>correct shape</u> to fit into the active site.
3) <u>Only one substrate</u> will be the correct shape to fit, so each enzyme only catalyses one specific reaction.
4) Anything that <u>changes</u> the shape of the active site will <u>affect</u> how well the enzyme works.

The Effect of Temperature on Enzyme Activity

As temperature <u>increases</u>, enzyme reactions become <u>faster</u>, because the molecules have more <u>energy</u>. However, at high temperatures the atoms of the enzyme molecule vibrate more rapidly and <u>break</u> the weak bonds that hold the <u>tertiary structure</u> together. The <u>shape</u> of the active site <u>changes</u> and the substrate can no longer fit in. The enzyme is said to be <u>denatured</u>.

The Effect of pH on Enzyme Activity

<u>Acids</u> and <u>alkalis</u> can denature enzymes. Hydrogen ions (H^+) in acids and hydroxyl ions (OH^-) in alkalis disrupt the <u>weak bonds</u> and change the shape of the active site.

Test your understanding with the questions below:

1) Look at the diagram above then describe the enzyme-substrate complex.
2) Explain why a denatured enzyme will not function.

<u>Answers</u>

1) The substrate is attached to the active site of the enzyme and the enzyme has moulded itself around the substrate to make a perfect fit.
2) The shape of the active site has changed and the substrate will no longer fit.

Plant and Animal Cells

You Can See Cell Structure with a Light Microscope

Cells have different features so they can carry out different functions — but many features are common to all cells. A light microscope can magnify up to 1500 times and allows you to see individual animal, plant and bacterial cells.

1) If the cells have been stained you can see the dark coloured nucleus surrounded by lighter coloured cytoplasm.
2) Tiny mitochondria and the black line of the cell membrane are also visible.
3) In plant cells, the cell wall, chloroplasts and the vacuole can be seen.

4 things animal and plant cells have in common:

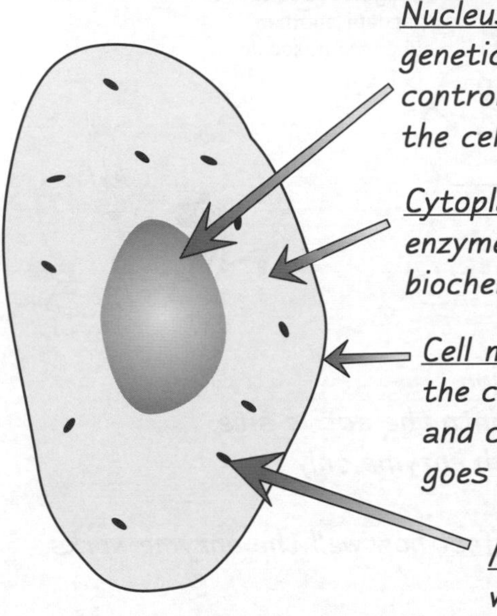

Nucleus contains genetic material that controls what the cell does.

Cytoplasm contains enzymes that speed up biochemical reactions.

Cell membrane holds the cell together and controls what goes in and out.

Mitochondria are where glucose and oxygen are used to produce energy.

3 extras that only plant cells have:

Rigid cell wall made of cellulose, gives the cell support.

Vacuole contains cell sap, a weak solution of sugar and salts.

Chloroplasts contain chlorophyll for photosynthesis. They're found in the green parts of plants, e.g. leaves and stem.

Electron Microscopes have a Greater Magnification

You may have thought that cytoplasm was pretty boring stuff but in fact it is packed full of tiny organelles (little organs) like mitochondria, ribosomes and endoplasmic reticulum.

1) Each type of organelle has a special function within the cell.
2) The detailed ultrastructure of cells was revealed in the 1950s when the electron microscope was invented.
3) An electron microscope can magnify objects up to 1 500 000 times and, more importantly, it allows greater detail to be seen. The image that's recorded is called an electron micrograph.

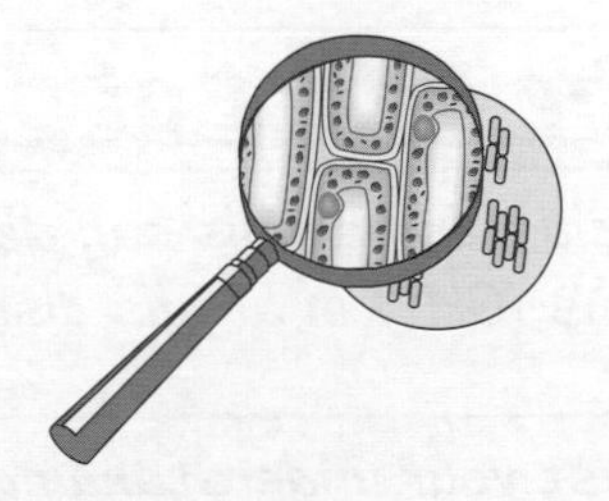

Have a go at these questions:

1) Name three things visible with a light microscope in both animal and plant cells.
2) Which type of microscope must be used to show the detailed ultrastructure of a cell?

Answers

1) Any 3 from: nucleus, cell membrane, cytoplasm, mitochondria.
2) An electron microscope.

Function of Nucleus, Mitochondria and Cell Wall

Nucleus

1) The nucleus is the control centre of the cell.
2) It contains DNA (deoxyribonucleic acid), the coded information needed for making proteins.
3) During cell division the chromosomes carrying the long DNA molecules coil up, becoming shorter and thicker and visible with a light microscope.
4) Electron micrographs show that there's a double membrane around the nucleus.
5) Organisms made up of cells with a true nucleus are said to be eukaryotic (pronounced like this: you-carry-ot-ick). All plant and animal cells are eukaryotic.
6) Organisms without a membrane around their DNA, like bacteria, are prokaryotic (pro-carry-ot-ick).

Mitochondria

Mitochondria are about the size of bacteria, so they can be seen with a light microscope, but you need an electron microscope to see any of the detail.
Each mitochondrion has a smooth outer membrane and a folded inner membrane:

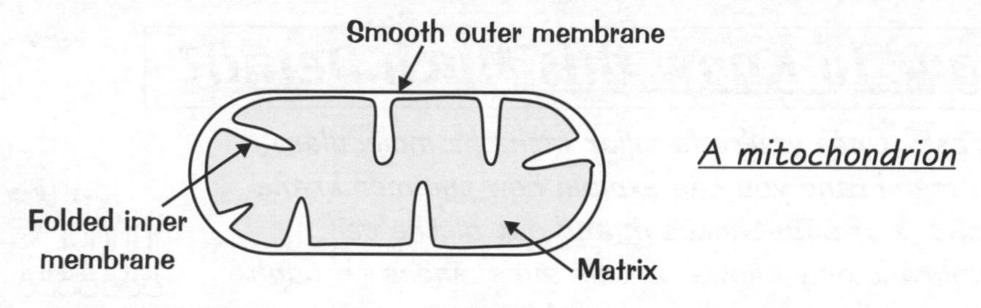

A mitochondrion

Aerobic respiration occurs inside the mitochondria.

Word equation: GLUCOSE + OXYGEN → ENERGY + CARBON DIOXIDE + WATER

Their job is to capture the energy in glucose in a form that the cell can use. The energy ends up in molecules of ATP (adenosine triphosphate). ATP is used in the cell to provide the energy for muscle contraction, active transport (called active uptake in some text books) and building large molecules from small ones, as well as many other processes.

Cell Wall

1) The cell wall is relatively rigid and provides support for the plant cell.
2) It mainly consists of bundles of long, straight cellulose molecules.
3) The cellulose molecules lay side by side to form microfibrils.

Check you can remember it all by answering the questions below:

1) Which organelle contains DNA?
2) In which organelle does aerobic respiration occur?

Answers
1) The nucleus.
2) The mitochondria.

Cell Membranes

Structure of the Cell Membrane

The cell membrane is the very thin structure around an individual cell.
Don't confuse it with body membranes, which are made up from layers of whole cells.

1) Electron micrographs show that the cell membrane consists of a double layer of phospholipid molecules tightly packed together.
2) Bigger protein molecules are embedded in the phospholipid molecules.
3) Some proteins go all the way through the membrane and some only go halfway.

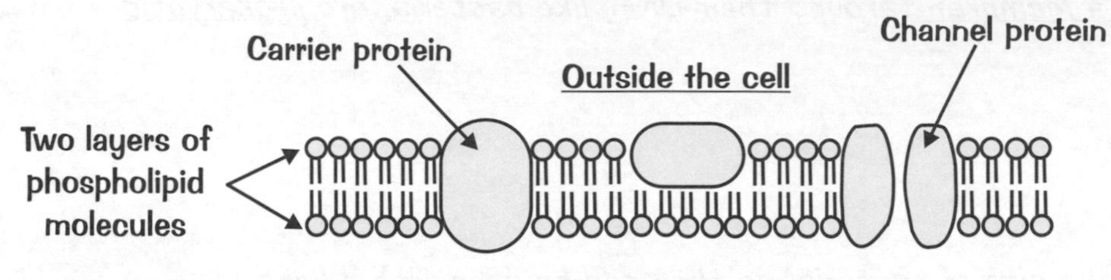

Cell membranes can also be called plasma membranes.

Do I Really have to Know this Much Detail?

1) The answer is "Yes". Once you're familiar with the molecular structure of the membrane you can explain how the membrane controls the passage of substances in and out of the cell.
2) Because the membrane only allows certain substances through it, it's described as being partially permeable.

Substances Pass Through Membranes by Four Methods

1 Diffusion

1) The particles of liquids and gases are constantly moving about. This movement causes the particles to spread from an area of higher concentration to an area of lower concentration.
2) Particles will diffuse through the cell membrane as long as they are small enough to pass through the very small gaps between the phospholipid molecules.
Water, oxygen and carbon dioxide molecules can do this.
3) The cell doesn't need to provide any energy for this process.

The difference in concentration is sometimes called concentration gradient, e.g. a big difference in concentration — a big concentration gradient.

2 Osmosis

Osmosis is the diffusion of water molecules across a partially permeable membrane from a region of higher concentration of water molecules to a region of lower concentration of water molecules. The cell doesn't need to provide energy.

Cell Membranes

3) Facilitated Diffusion

1) Glucose and many other water soluble molecules are too big to diffuse across the membrane by themselves. They must be helped across by carrier proteins.
2) Each substance has its own specific carrier protein.
3) For example, a molecule of glucose fits onto the outside end of a glucose carrier protein.
4) This causes the protein to change shape, allowing the glucose molecule to diffuse through it into the cytoplasm of the cell. The cell doesn't need to provide any energy.

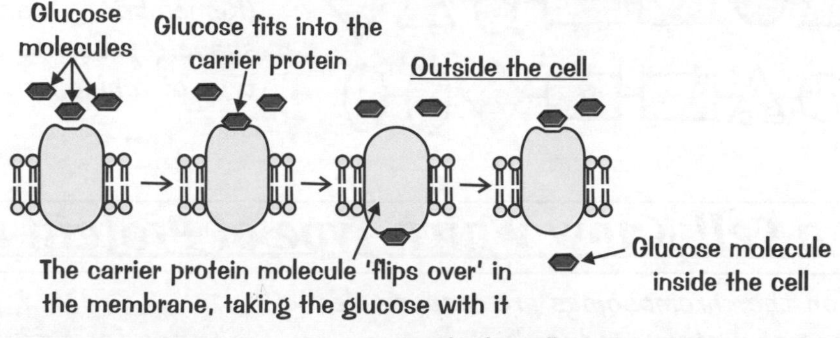

Mineral ions like sodium (Na^+) and potassium (K^+) have electrical charges on them, so they also need help to cross the membrane. Specific channel proteins in the membrane allow them to diffuse through.

4) Active Transport (or Active Uptake)

1) When a cell needs to move substances across the membrane from a region of low concentration to a region of higher concentration, it must provide energy.
2) The substance fits into a specific carrier protein, then molecules of ATP provide the energy to change the shape of the protein.
3) As it changes shape the protein actively transports the substance across the membrane.
4) These special carrier proteins are sometimes called "pumps" because they're moving substances against a concentration gradient.

Answer the quick quiz below:

1) Name the two types of molecule that make up the cell membrane.
2) Give four ways substances can cross cell membranes.
3) What do you call the diffusion of water molecules through the cell membrane?
4) What must the cell provide for active transport?

Answers

1) Phospholipids and protein molecules.
2) Diffusion, osmosis, facilitated diffusion and active transport.
3) Osmosis.
4) Energy (ATP).

The Genetic Code

What Causes Different Characteristics in Organisms?

1) All characteristics are due to proteins.
2) Different proteins are responsible for different characteristics.
3) Proteins are all made up of chains of amino acids.
4) It's the order of the amino acids in a protein that determines its structure, and hence how it works.

Protein A

Protein B

(Remember — each different shape represents a different type of amino acid.)

How does a Cell Know Which Type of Protein to Produce?

1) The genes on the chromosomes are responsible for the types of protein produced.
2) Genes are sets of coded instructions for building proteins.
3) One gene codes for one protein.

'Codes for' just means 'contains the instructions for'.

How Does the Code Work?

Unravel a chromosome and you have a very long molecule called DNA (deoxyribonucleic acid). The DNA molecule is shaped like a twisted ladder, with each "rung" made from two chemicals called bases. There are four different bases; A, T, C and G:

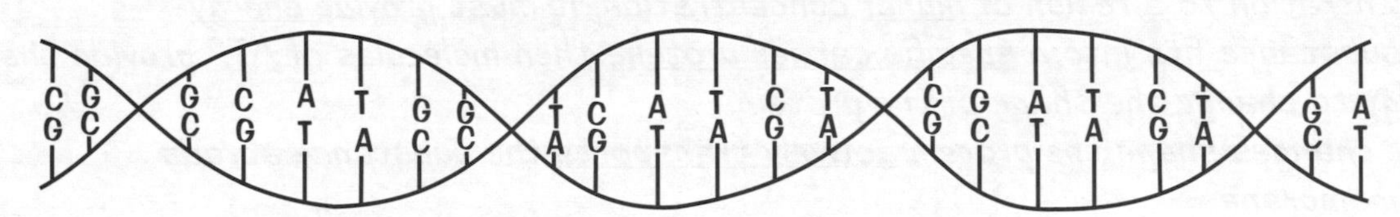

A gene is a short section of DNA. The sequence of the bases in that section of the DNA determines the order in which the amino acids are put together in a particular protein.

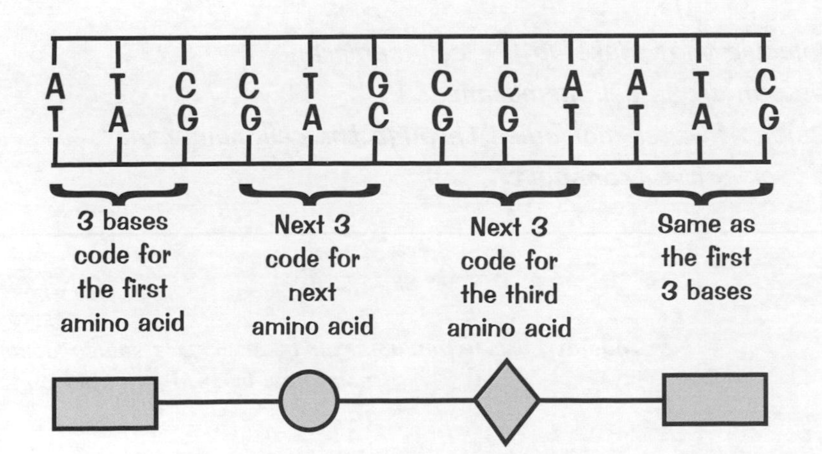

Three bases (a triplet) in a row code for one amino acid.

The Genetic Code

Mutations are Changes in the Code

If the order of the bases in the gene is changed then the sequence of the amino acids in the protein will be changed. The protein will have a different shape and that may affect the way it works.

> *E.g. people with cystic fibrosis have a gene with three bases missing. Remember, three bases code for one amino acid, so the protein that's produced has one amino acid missing. The abnormal protein can't function properly and, as a result, the mucus in the lungs and digestive system is very thick and sticky.*

Changes in the sequence or in the number of bases in a gene are called mutations. They occur naturally and, although most are harmful, some are neutral in their effect. In rare cases, a mutation can be responsible for a characteristic that's beneficial and increases the chances of survival of an organism and any offspring that inherit the mutant gene.

Increasing the Rate of Mutation

Ionising radiation (including X-rays, ultraviolet light and alpha, beta and gamma radiation from radioactive materials) and certain chemicals can damage or destroy DNA molecules. They are called mutagens. The greater the exposure to a mutagen, the greater the chance of mutation.

Cancer is Caused by Mutations

1) *Cell division is controlled by proteins (which are produced from genes).*
2) *If mutations occur in these genes the proteins produced might not work properly.*
3) *The cells divide uncontrollably, forming a mass of cells called a tumour. Some tumours can invade other areas of the body. These tumours are called cancers.*

Test your understanding with the questions below:

1) *What is a gene?*
2) *Suggest why scientists refer to the genetic code as a triplet code.*
3) *What is a mutation?*
4) *What is a mutagen?*
5) *Name one disease caused by mutations.*

Answers

1) A gene is a section of DNA that codes for a particular protein.
2) It's called a triplet code because three bases make up the code for one amino acid.
3) A mutation is a change in the base sequence of a gene.
4) A mutagen is a substance or type of radiation that can damage DNA.
5) E.g. cystic fibrosis, cancer.

DNA and Chromosomes

DNA is Found on Chromosomes

DNA is found in the nucleus of eukaryotic cells and in the cytoplasm of prokaryotic cells. It has to be wound up into chromosomes to fit in. Each human chromosome contains between a couple of hundred and a few thousand genes.

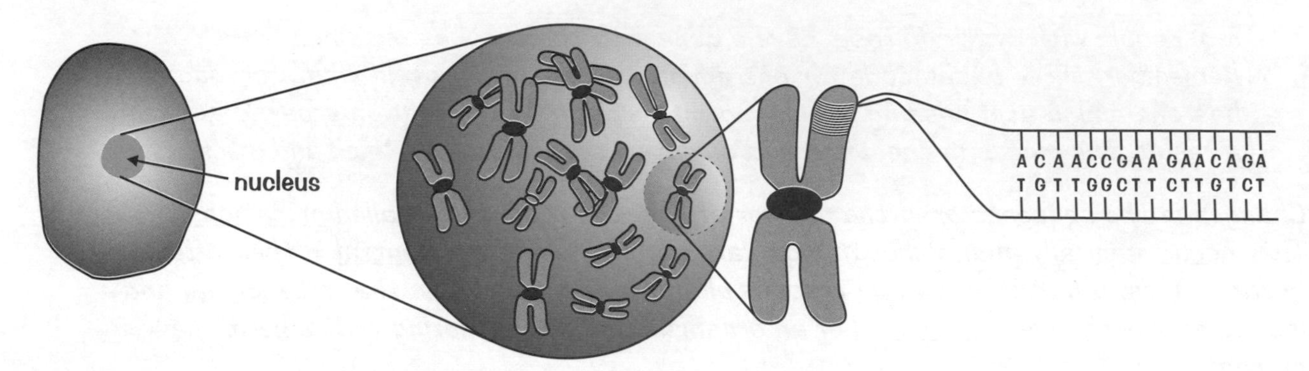

Homologous Pairs

Humans have 23 homologous pairs of chromosomes (46 in total), e.g. two number 1s, two number 2s, two number 3s etc. One from each pair comes from your mother and one comes from your father. Both chromosomes in a pair are the same size and carry the same genes (which is why they're called homologous pairs). But they usually have different alleles (different versions of the genes).

Chromosomes are Often Shown as X Shaped

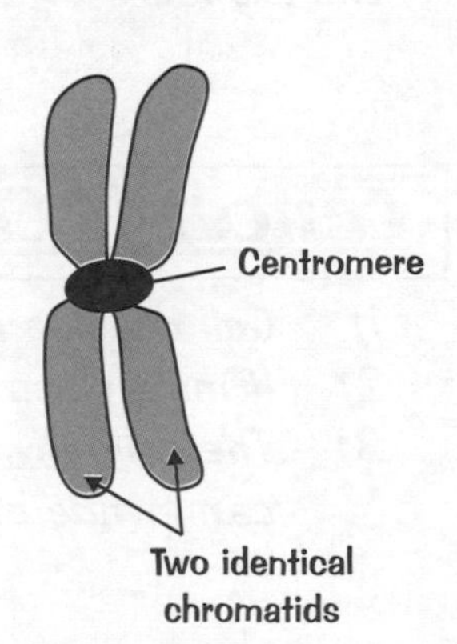

In loads of books chromosomes are shown as X shaped. An X shaped chromosome is actually one chromosome attached to an identical copy of itself. Don't get it confused with a homologous pair of chromosomes. They're only X shaped just after the DNA has been replicated (e.g. in cell division). Each side of the X is referred to as a chromatid and the bit in the middle where they're attached is called the centromere.

Have a go at these questions:

1) Where is DNA found in a eukaryotic cell?
2) How many homologous pairs of chromosomes do human cells have?
3) Are homologous pairs of chromosomes identical? Explain your answer.
4) What is a chromatid?
5) What is the name of the region where two identical chromatids are joined?

Answers

1) In the nucleus.
2) 23.
3) No. They're the same size and carry the same genes but they usually have different alleles.
4) An identical copy of a chromosome.
5) Centromere.

Cell Division — Mitosis

Mitosis is Needed for Growth and Repair

1) If you have damaged tissue, the cells around the damaged area divide by mitosis to replace the damaged cells.
2) Cells also divide by mitosis to produce new tissue for growth.

Asexual Reproduction Involves Mitosis

1) In asexual reproduction, a single organism produces offspring by dividing into two organisms or by splitting off a piece of itself.
2) All the offspring are genetically identical to each other and to the parent.
3) The cells divide by mitosis (like most cells).

Bacteria and many plants reproduce asexually.

In Mitosis the DNA Copies Itself Then the Cell Divides Once

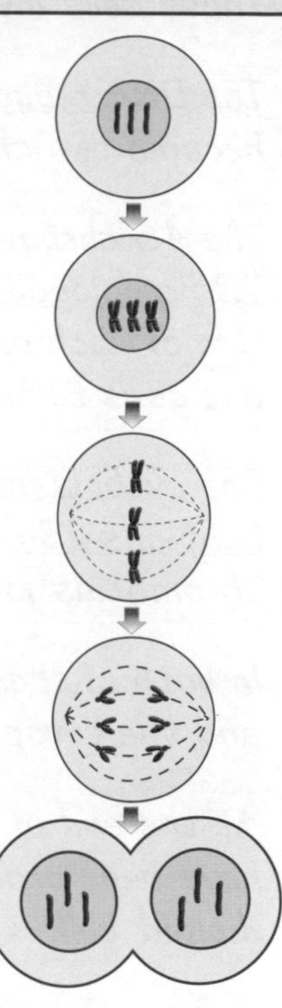

1) Before the cell starts to divide, every DNA molecule (each chromosome) must replicate so that each new cell has a full copy of DNA. The new molecule remains attached to the original one at the centromere.

2) Each DNA molecule becomes supercoiled and compact. Each chromosome can now be seen with a light microscope and appears as two chromatids lying side by side, joined by the centromere (i.e. X shaped).

3) The nuclear membrane breaks down and the chromosomes line up along the equator (middle) of the cell.

4) The centromeres split and the chromatids separate and are dragged to opposite ends of the cell.

5) A nuclear membrane forms around each set of chromatids (exact copies of the original chromosomes) and the cytoplasm divides.

Answer the quick quiz below:

1) Give three uses of mitosis.
2) Why is DNA replicated before cell division can occur?
3) Do the homologous pairs separate in mitosis?
4) How many cells are produced when a cell divides by mitosis?

Answers

1) Growth, repair, asexual reproduction.
2) So each new cell has a full copy of DNA.
3) No (the chromatids separate).
4) Two.

Cell Division — Meiosis

Sexual Reproduction Involves Meiosis

1) *In sexual reproduction, the offspring are genetically different from their parents and from each other. This produces variation in a population.*
2) *Each parent produces sex cells (gametes) containing just one set of genetic material. This involves a special kind of cell division, called meiosis, and the gametes are described as being haploid.*
3) *During fertilisation the nuclei of the gametes join together to form a zygote. The zygote has two complete sets of genetic material, and is said to be diploid.*
4) *The zygote grows by simple cell division (mitosis) to form the embryo.*

In Meiosis, DNA Copies Itself Then the Cell Divides Twice

1) *The only cells in the human body that divide by meiosis are special cells in the testes and ovaries.*

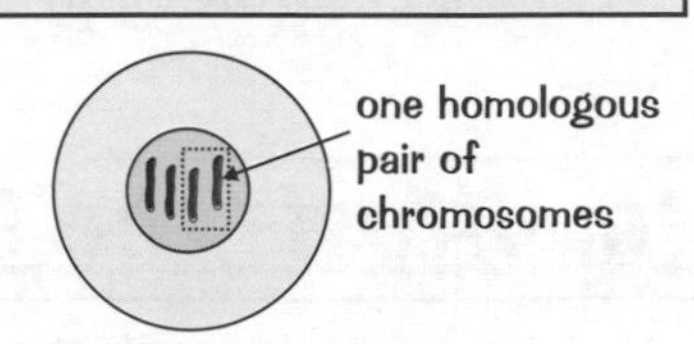

2) *These cells divide to produce gametes (e.g. sperm and eggs).*

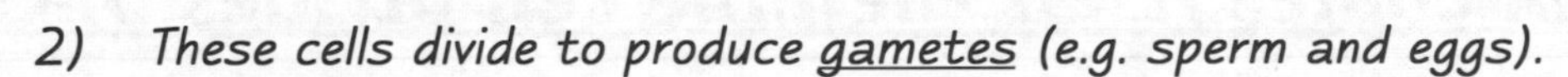

3) *The DNA replicates, so each of the 46 chromosomes become two chromatids joined by a centromere.*

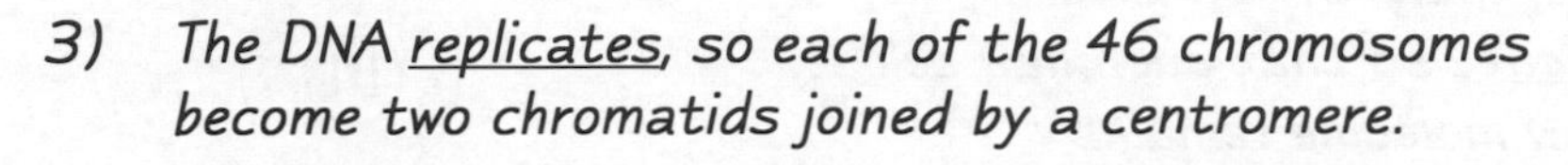

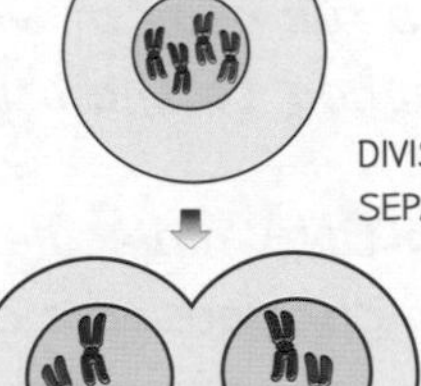

4) *The 46 chromosomes sort themselves into the 23 homologous pairs, then the pairs separate. One of each pair goes to one side of the cell and one goes to the other.*

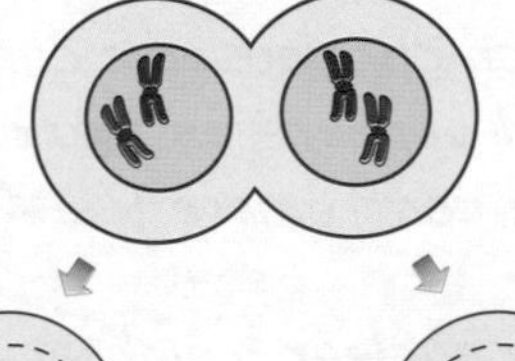

5) *The cytoplasm now divides. Each of the new cells contains 23 chromosomes (consisting of two chromatids joined by a centromere).*

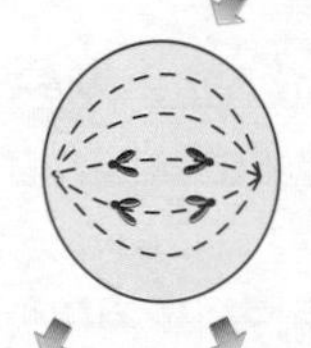

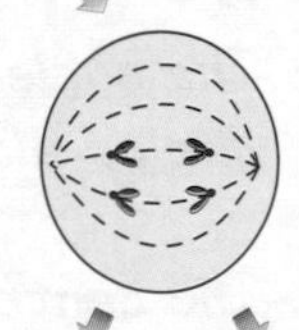

6) *In both of these new cells the chromatids separate and the cytoplasm divides to form two cells.*

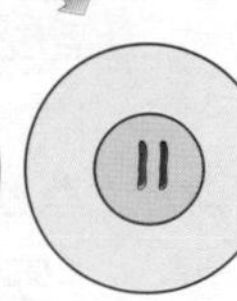

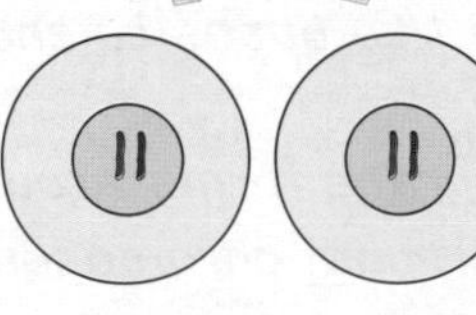

7) *At the end of meiosis, four haploid cells have been produced from every original diploid cell.*

See if you can answer these questions:

1) *Are gametes haploid or diploid?*
2) *Where in the human body does meiosis occur?*
3) *How many cell divisions are there in meiosis?*
4) *How many cells are produced when a cell divides by meiosis?*

Answers

1) *Haploid.*
2) *In the testes and the ovaries.*
3) *Two.*
4) *Four.*

Diet and the Digestive System

Composition of Food

You need to eat a healthy, balanced diet to provide your body with all the energy and nutrients it needs for running, jumping, reading CGP books...
A balanced diet should contain:

1) Carbohydrates — e.g. found in bread and sweets. Needed for energy.
2) Fats (lipids) — e.g. found in butter and oil. Needed for energy storage.
3) Proteins — e.g. found in chicken and eggs. Needed for growth.
4) Vitamins and minerals — e.g. calcium (found in milk and cheese) for healthy bone growth. Different vitamins and minerals have different functions.
5) Water — needed for the chemical reactions that take place in your body.
6) Fibre — e.g. found in vegetables and cereals. Helps food to move through the gut.

Digestion

The human digestive system has three functions:

1) The mechanical breakdown of large pieces of food.
2) The chemical breakdown of large food molecules into smaller molecules.
3) The absorption of small food molecules into the bloodstream.

Digestion is the chemical breakdown of large molecules into small molecules.

The chemical reactions involved in digestion are hydrolysis reactions (water is used during the reaction).

The gut is simply a long, muscular tube that starts at the mouth and finishes at the anus:

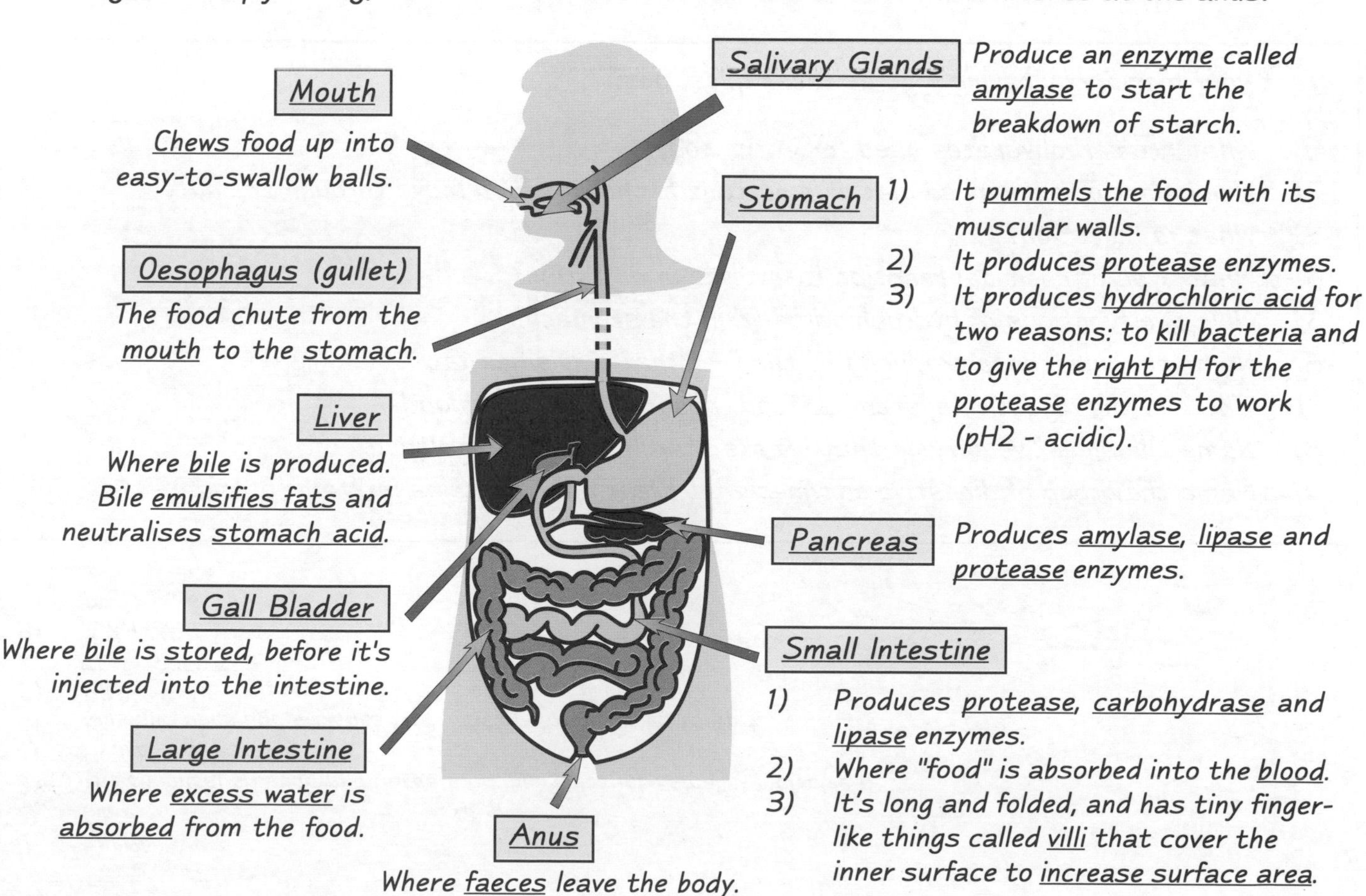

Digestive Enzymes

Digestive Enzymes

The digestive system contains lots of different enzymes that break down large food molecules into smaller molecules, which can be absorbed into the blood. They work by breaking the bonds that hold the larger molecules together. There are three main types of digestive enzymes:

1) *Carbohydrases — break down complex carbohydrates (polysaccharides) into smaller molecules (disaccharides and monosaccharides), e.g. amylase breaks down starch into maltose.*

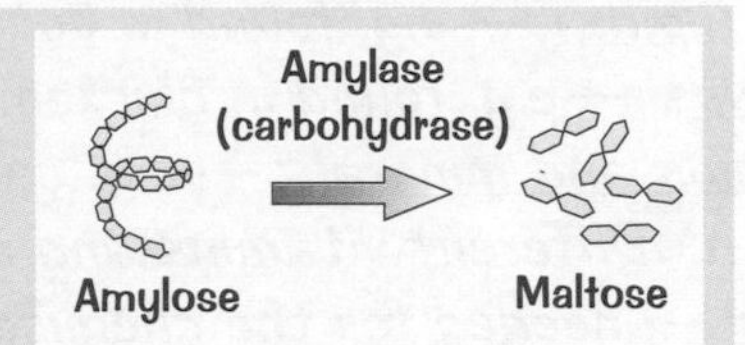

2) *Lipases — break down lipids (fats) into fatty acids and glycerol, e.g. pancreatic lipase.*

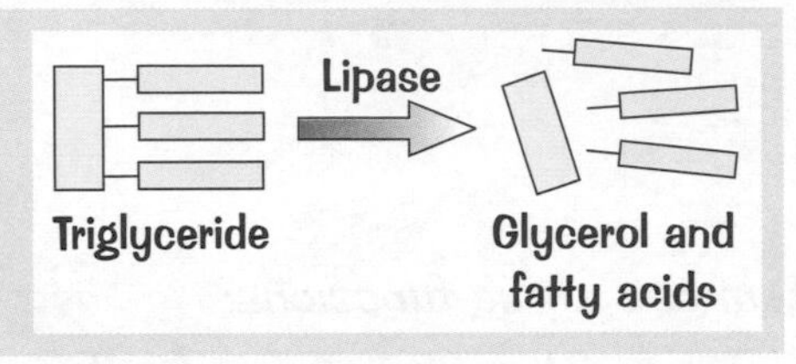

3) *Proteases — break down proteins into smaller chains or amino acids.*

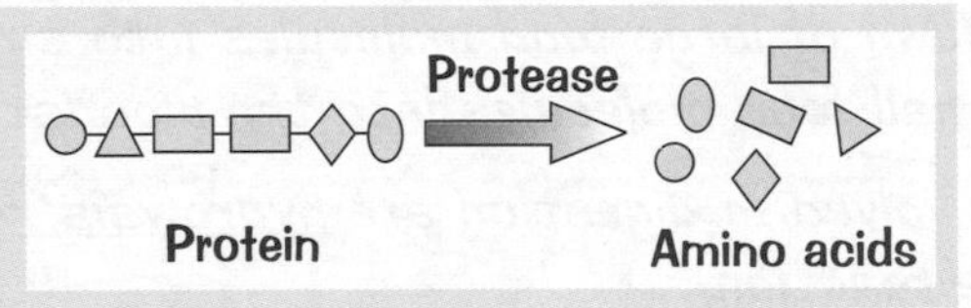

Test your memory by having a go at these questions:

1) *What are carbohydrates used for in the body?*
2) *Which part of a balanced diet is important for helping food move through the gut?*
3) *What is digestion?*
4) *What type of chemical reaction is involved in digestion?*
5) *Give two functions of hydrochloric acid in the stomach.*
6) *Name the substance produced by the liver that emulsifies fat.*
7) *Where in the digestive system is "food" absorbed into the blood?*
8) *Name the digestive enzyme that breaks starch down into maltose.*
9) *Name the group of digestive enzymes that break down proteins into amino acids.*

Answers

1) *Energy.*
2) *Fibre.*
3) *The chemical breakdown of large food molecules into smaller molecules.*
4) *Hydrolysis reaction.*
5) *Kills microbes and provides the right pH for enzymes to work.*
6) *Bile.*
7) *The small intestine.*
8) *Amylase.*
9) *Proteases.*

Disease

Disease can be Caused by Many Things

1) Pathogens — these are organisms that can cause disease, e.g. bacteria and viruses. Infectious diseases are caused by pathogens and can be passed from person to person, e.g. TB, malaria and HIV.
2) Genetic defects — some diseases are caused by mutations in a person's genes, e.g. cystic fibrosis is caused by a mutation in a gene for a protein.
3) Lifestyle — lifestyle can cause lots of different diseases. Certain lifestyles also increase the risk of getting some diseases, e.g. smokers are more likely to get lung cancer.

Risk Factors for Disease

1) A risk factor is something that increases the chances of something bad happening. For example, smoking is a risk factor for heart disease — if you smoke you're more likely to get heart disease.
2) Risk factors don't always lead to disease though. For example, using sunbeds is a risk factor for skin cancer — if you use sunbeds you increase your risk of skin cancer, but you won't necessarily get the disease.
3) Some risk factors are unavoidable because they're inherited, e.g. certain versions of genes increase your risk of getting breast cancer. Some risk factors are avoidable because they're associated with your lifestyle. For example, a diet high in salt is a risk factor for high blood pressure — if you change your lifestyle to reduce your salt intake you reduce the risk.

Here's a table showing some common lifestyle risk factors and the diseases they're associated with:

Risk factor	Diseases
Smoking	Mouth, lung and throat cancer, emphysema and other lung diseases, cardiovascular disease
Drinking too much alcohol	Mouth, stomach, liver and breast cancer, possibly many other cancers, cardiovascular disease
High blood pressure	Cardiovascular disease, diabetes
Overweight/obese	Various cancers, cardiovascular disease, diabetes
Unbalanced diet	Various cancers, cardiovascular disease, diabetes
Using sun beds too much	Skin cancer

Have a go at these questions:

1) What are pathogens?
2) Give an example of an infectious disease.
3) What is a risk factor?
4) List two diseases that smoking is a risk factor for.

Answers

1) Organisms that can cause disease.
2) E.g. TB, malaria, HIV.
3) Something that increases the chances of something bad happening.
4) Any 2 from: mouth, lung and throat cancer, emphysema and other lung diseases, cardiovascular disease.

Immunity

Phagocytes Engulf Pathogens

1) If a pathogen gets into the body it's detected by a type of white blood cell called a phagocyte.
2) It's actually the molecules on the surface of the pathogen that the phagocytes detect. These molecules are called antigens.
3) Human cells have antigens on their surface too but phagocytes can tell the difference between 'self' (your own) and 'foreign' antigens.
4) Phagocytes engulf the pathogen carrying the foreign antigen and destroys it.

There are lots of different types of white blood cells.

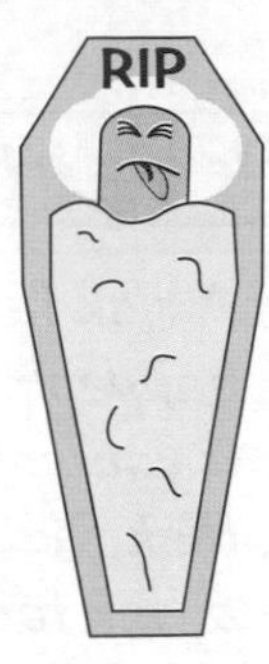

White Blood Cells Produce Antibodies

1) Some white blood cells produce antibodies that bind to antigens.
2) The ones that produce antibodies are called B-cells (they're sometimes called B-lymphocytes — pronounced: lim-fo-sites).
3) When the antibody binds to the antigen it brings about the death of the pathogen carrying it.

Another Type of White Blood Cell is Involved

1) T-cells (or T-lymphocytes) are a type of white blood cell that are involved in communication between phagocytes and B-cells.
2) When a phagocyte has engulfed a pathogen it signals to the T-cell that it's found something. The T-cell then activates the B-cells to produce antibodies.

Vaccination Gives You Immunity

1) If you're vaccinated against a pathogen you can't get that disease (you're immune).
2) Vaccines contain antigens from a pathogen in a form that can't harm you, e.g. attached to dead bacteria.
3) Your body produces antibodies against the antigens so if the same pathogen (carrying the same antigens) tries to invade again the immune system can respond really quickly and you won't suffer from any symptoms.
4) Vaccines don't stop the pathogen getting into the body, they just get rid of it really quickly when it does.

Try answering the quick quiz below:

1) What do phagocytes detect?
2) What kind of white blood cells produce antibodies?
3) What is the role of T-cells?
4) What do vaccines contain?

Answers

1) Foreign antigens.
2) B-cells (B-lymphocytes).
3) To communicate between phagocytes and B-cells / to activate B-cells.
4) Antigens from a pathogen.

Size and the Surface Area to Volume Ratio

Small Objects have Relatively Large Surface Areas

1) Have you ever wondered why there are no large single-celled organisms or why big animals are made up of millions of tiny cells instead of a few large ones?
2) The main reason relates to the changes in the surface area to volume ratio of an object as it increases in size.
3) Look at the three cubes in the diagram below. The smallest cube has the biggest surface area to volume ratio and the biggest cube has the smallest surface area to volume ratio.

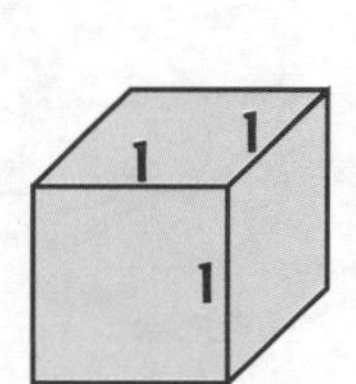

Surface area 6 cm^2
Volume 1 cm^3
Surface area : Volume
6 : 1

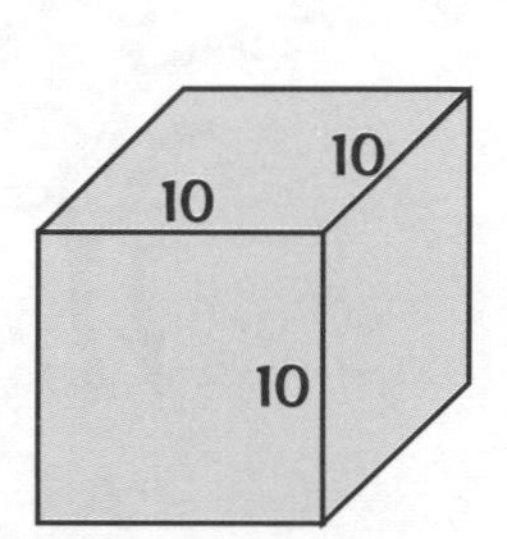

Surface area 600 cm^2
Volume 1000 cm^3
Surface area : Volume
0.6 : 1

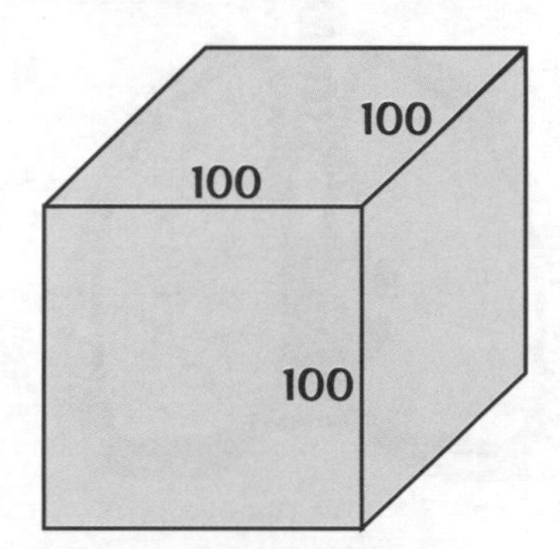

Surface area 60,000 cm^2
Volume 1,000,000 cm^3
Surface area : Volume
0.06 : 1

Surface Area is Important for Exchange

1) Cells or organisms need to exchange materials and heat with their environment.
2) More chemical reactions happen every second in organisms with a larger volume than in ones with smaller volumes.
3) Therefore more oxygen, nutrients, waste products and heat need to be exchanged across the membrane of cells of larger organisms.
4) With increasing volume this becomes an ever-increasing problem.

See if you can answer the questions below:

1) Which has the bigger surface area to volume ratio, a small organism or a large organism?
2) Which animal has the greatest surface area: volume ratio — Animal A 9.8:1, Animal B 0.98:1?
3) In the Arctic which animal will find it easier to keep warm — an adult male polar bear or an adult male arctic fox? Explain your answer.

Answers

1) A small organism.
2) Animal A.
3) The polar bear. It is larger than the fox so it has a smaller surface area to volume ratio than the fox. The bear's rate of heat loss will be less than that of the fox.

Structure of the Thorax

Lungs have a Very Large Gas Exchange Surface

Large, active animals, like mammals, have evolved complex blood systems and lungs to provide a large surface area for the efficient diffusion of oxygen and carbon dioxide.

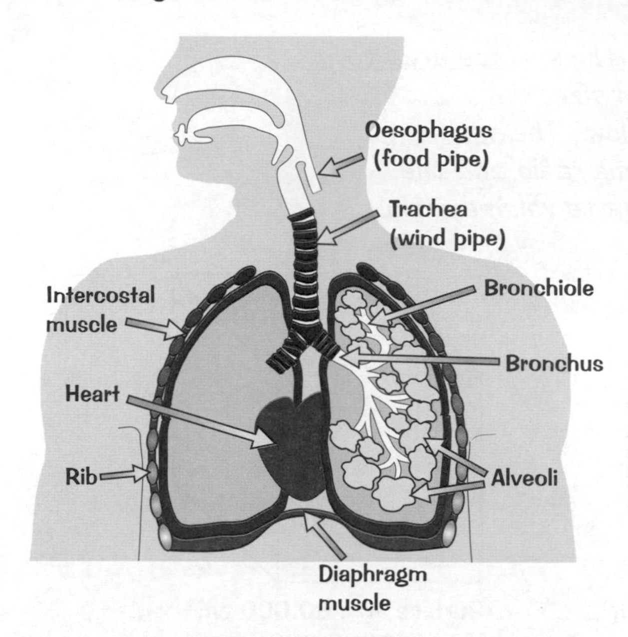

Gas exchange takes place in millions of tiny air sacs, called alveoli.

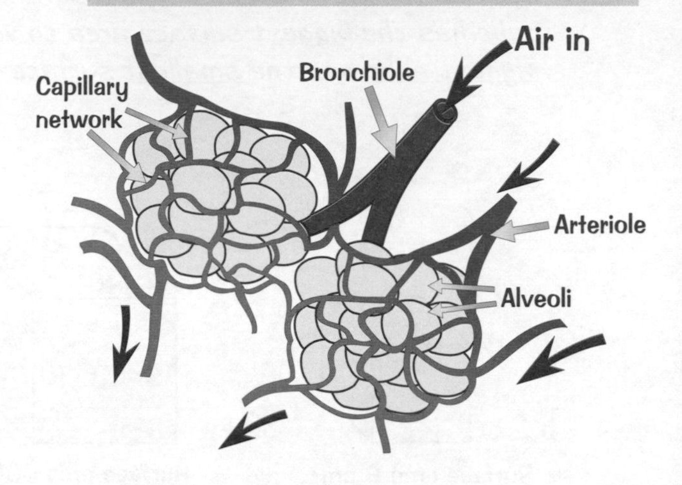

Alveoli have Adaptations that Increase the Diffusion Rate

1) *The walls of the alveoli consist of a single layer of thin, flattened, epithelial cells. Diffusion happens faster when molecules only have to travel short distances.*
2) *Diffusion is faster when there's a bigger difference in concentrations between two regions. The blood flowing through the rich network of capillaries around the alveoli carries away the oxygen that has diffused through the alveolar walls. This ensures that there's always a higher concentration of oxygen inside the alveoli than in the blood. The reverse is true for carbon dioxide.*
3) *The alveolar walls are fully permeable to dissolved gases. Oxygen and carbon dioxide can pass easily through the cell membranes of the epithelial cells.*

Have a go at these questions:

1) *In which part of the lungs does gas exchange take place?*
2) *Describe the shape of the cells that make up the walls of the alveoli and explain how their shape suits their function.*
3) *Name two gases that can pass easily through the epithelial cell membranes.*

Answers

1) The alveoli.
2) The epithelial cells are thin and flattened. The gases can diffuse quickly because the distance is small.
3) Oxygen and carbon dioxide.

Breathing In and Breathing Out

Why do We Need to Breathe?

Ventilation ensures that air with a high concentration of oxygen is taken into the lungs and air with a high concentration of carbon dioxide is removed from the lungs. This maintains high concentration gradients between air and blood, increasing the rate of diffusion of oxygen and carbon dioxide.

If Volume Increases, Air Pressure Decreases

If the volume of an enclosed space is increased, the pressure inside it will decrease.

1) *The lungs are suspended in the airtight thorax.*
2) *Increasing the volume of the thorax decreases the air pressure in the lungs to below atmospheric pressure. Air flows into the lungs, inflating them until the pressure in the alveoli equals that of the atmosphere.*
3) *Decreasing the volume of the thorax increases the pressure in the lungs and air flows out until the pressure in the alveoli drops to atmospheric pressure.*

Breathing In...

1) *Intercostal muscles and diaphragm contract.*
2) *Thorax volume increases.*
3) *This decreases the pressure, so air flows in.*

...and Breathing Out

1) *Intercostal muscles and diaphragm relax.*
2) *Thorax volume decreases.*
3) *This increases the pressure so air flows out.*

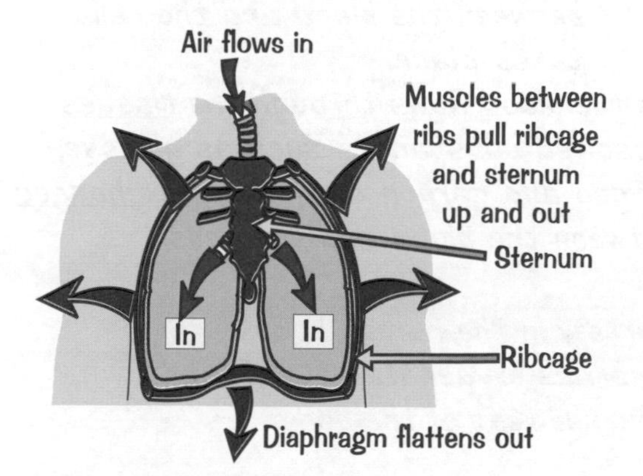

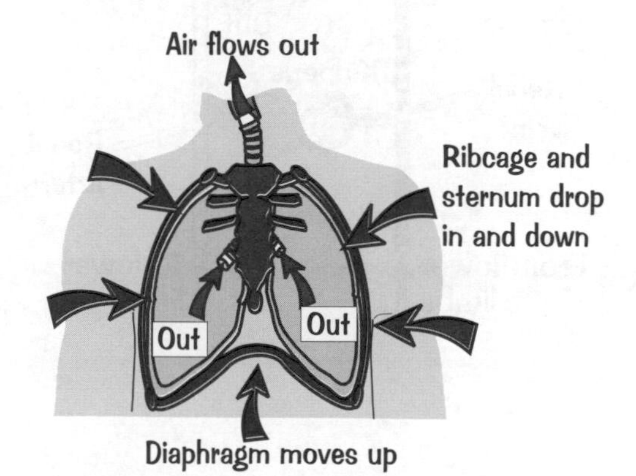

Take a deep breath and have a go at these:

1) *Describe the relationship between volume and pressure in an enclosed space.*
2) *Choose the correct word to complete the following sentence. Air always flows from a region of higher/lower pressure to a region of higher/lower pressure.*
3) *Which two sets of muscles contract when we breathe in?*
4) *Does breathing out require energy?*

Answers

1) *When the volume increases, the pressure decreases and when the volume decreases, the pressure increases.*
2) *Air always flows from a region of higher pressure to a region of lower pressure.*
3) *The intercostal muscles and the diaphragm muscles.*
4) *No.*

The Circulatory System

Large Animals Need a Circulatory System

1) Diffusion is only efficient over <u>short distances</u>, so any animal bigger than a simple worm needs a system that will bring glucose and oxygen into close contact with individual cells.
2) In humans, the <u>heart</u> pumps blood around the body through <u>blood vessels</u>.

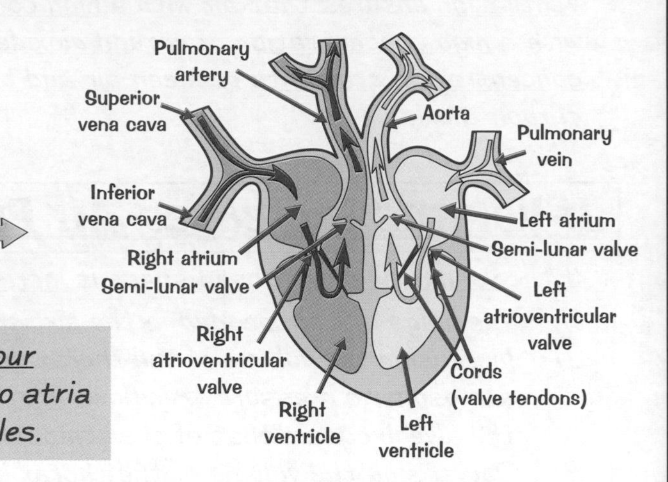

The heart has <u>four chambers</u> — two atria and two ventricles.

Brain, head and neck
Arms
Lungs
Pulmonary vein
Pulmonary artery
Aorta
Vena cava
Heart
Hepatic artery
Hepatic vein
Liver
Hepatic portal vein
Gut
Kidneys
Renal vein
Renal artery
From lower limbs
To lower limbs

3) The blood vessels carry blood around the <u>entire body</u> and go to <u>every organ</u> before returning the blood to the heart.
4) There are <u>three</u> main types of blood vessel:
   - <u>Arteries</u> carry blood <u>away</u> from the heart.
   - <u>Veins</u> carry blood <u>to</u> the heart.
   - <u>Capillaries</u> are where the exchange between the blood and the cells takes place.
5) As the blood flows through the <u>tissues</u>, dissolved substances such as glucose, oxygen and carbon dioxide are <u>exchanged</u> between the blood and the cells.

The main artery in the human body is the <u>aorta</u>. It carries oxygenated blood <u>from the heart</u> to the rest of the body.

Yey, another mini quiz:

1) Name the organ that pumps blood around the body.
2) Name the four chambers of the heart.
3) Name the three main types of blood vessel.
4) In which type of blood vessel are substances exchanged between the blood and the cells?

<u>Answers</u>

1) The heart.
2) The right and left atria, the right and left ventricles.
3) Arteries, veins and capillaries.
4) Capillaries.

The Heart

Important Facts to Remember

1) The heart acts like two separate pumps. The right side sends blood to the lungs and the left side pumps blood around the rest of the body.
2) Blood always flows from a region of higher pressure to a region of lower pressure.
3) Valves in the heart prevent the blood from flowing backwards.
4) No energy is required to make the valves work — it's the blood pressing on the valves that makes them open and close.

The Cardiac Cycle

The cardiac cycle is the sequence of events that occurs during one heartbeat.

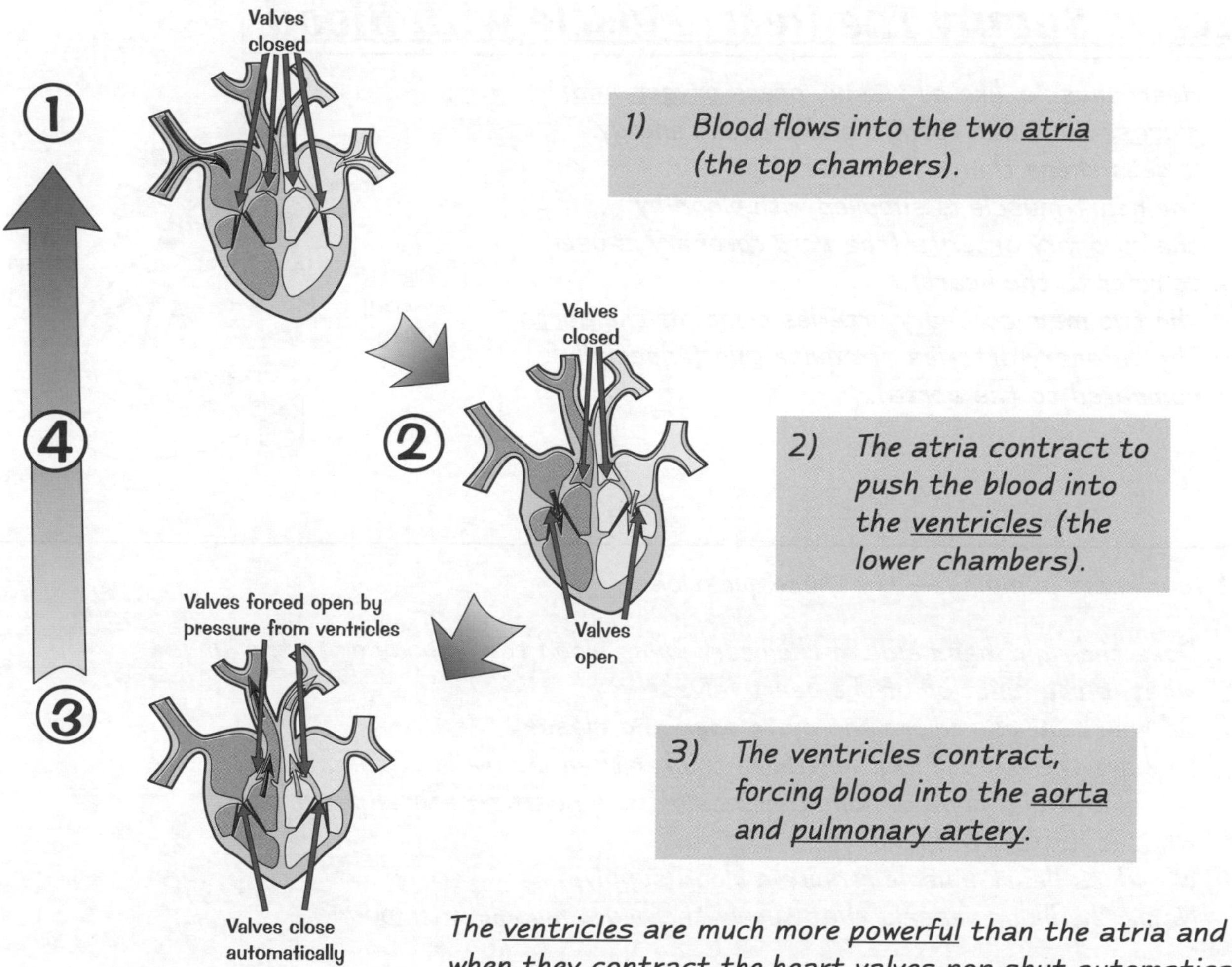

1) Blood flows into the two atria (the top chambers).

2) The atria contract to push the blood into the ventricles (the lower chambers).

3) The ventricles contract, forcing blood into the aorta and pulmonary artery.

4) The blood flows down the arteries, the atria fill again and the whole cycle starts over again.

The ventricles are much more powerful than the atria and when they contract the heart valves pop shut automatically to prevent backflow into the atria. The ventricle walls are thicker because they need to push the blood further (e.g. the left ventricle has to push blood all the way round the body).

As soon as the ventricles relax, the valves at the top of the heart pop shut to prevent backflow of blood (back into the ventricles) as it's now under a fair bit of pressure in the arteries.

The Heart

The Heart has its Own Pacemaker

1) Most muscles require nerve impulses from the central nervous system to make them contract.
2) The heart produces its own electrical impulses.
3) A group of specialised cells called the sino-atrial node, in the wall of the right atrium, sends out regular impulses.
4) These spread across the atria and down into the ventricles, making them contract.

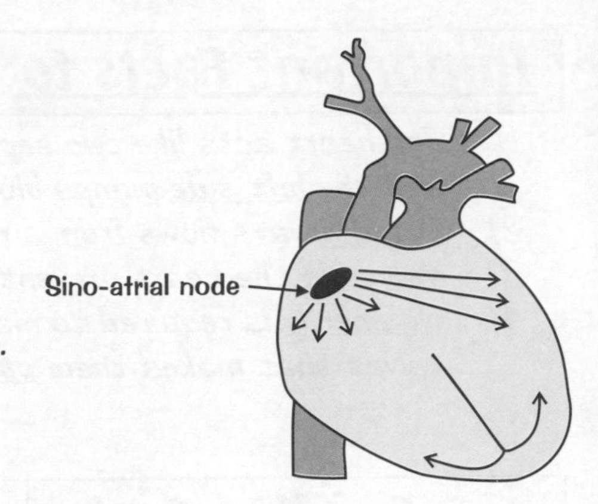

Arteries Supply The Heart Muscle with Blood

1) Heart muscle, like all tissue, needs oxygen and glucose so it can respire and produce energy.
2) It gets these things from the blood.
3) The heart muscle is supplied with blood by the coronary arteries (the word coronary is used to refer to the heart).
4) The two main coronary arteries come off the aorta.
5) The coronary arteries are quite thin (especially compared to the aorta).

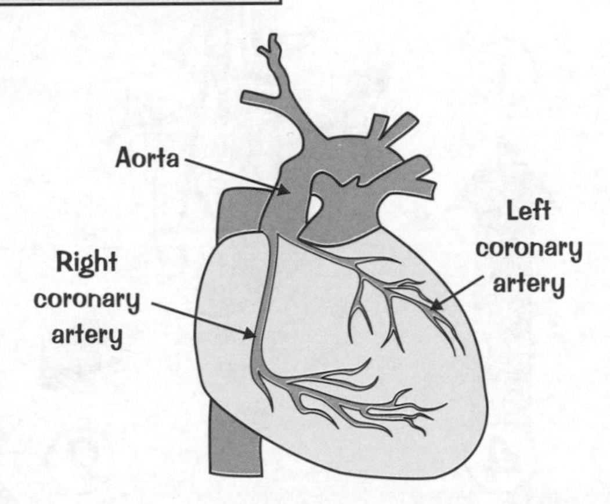

Get your heart pumping — try these questions:

1) Does the right hand side of the heart pump blood to the body or to the lungs?
2) What is the function of the heart valves?
3) Do heart valves require energy to open and close?
4) Why are the walls of the ventricles thicker than the walls of the atria?
5) The sino-atrial node is sometimes called the heart's natural pacemaker. What is its function?
6) Why does heart muscle require a blood supply?
7) Name the blood vessels that supply the heart muscle with blood?

Answers

1) Lungs.
2) To keep the blood flowing one way.
3) No.
4) Because the ventricles have to pump blood further than the atria.
5) The sino-atrial node produces the regular electrical impulses that make the atria and ventricles contract.
6) So it can get oxygen and glucose for respiration (for energy).
7) The coronary arteries.

Cardiovascular Disease

There are Lots of Types of Cardiovascular Disease

1) Cardiovascular diseases are diseases of the heart and the blood vessels (cardio means it's to do with the heart and vascular means it's to do with the blood vessels).
2) Sometimes cardiovascular disease is shortened to CVD.
3) Most types of CVD begin with the build up of fatty deposits in artery walls — called atheromas.
4) The fatty deposits partially block the lumen (the hole the blood flows through), restricting blood flow and increasing blood pressure.
5) The fatty deposits also make the walls of the arteries rough, which can cause blood clots to form.
6) The blood clot can block the artery where it's formed or it can travel in the blood to another artery and cause a block there instead.

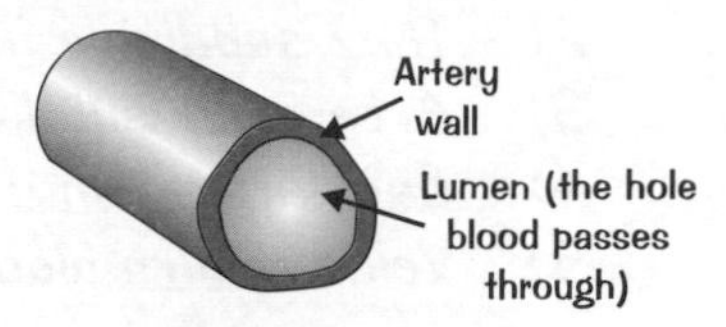

Cross section through a normal artery

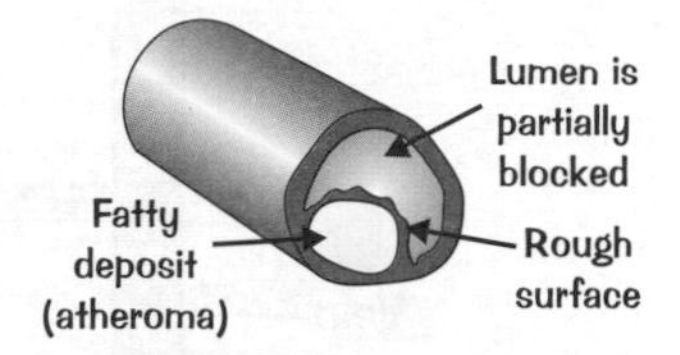

Cross section through blocked artery

You might come across these four common CVDs:

1) High Blood Pressure

Lots of things can cause high blood pressure (HBP) — atheromas, being overweight, an unbalanced diet, genes, etc. HBP can lead to other CVDs because blood clots are more likely to form if the blood's at high pressure.

2) Stroke

If a blood clot blocks an artery that supplies blood to the brain, it can cause a stroke — the brain tissue is damaged because of the lack of oxygen from the blood.

3) Coronary Heart Disease

Coronary heart disease (CHD) is when the coronary arteries become blocked by atheromas. This means the heart muscle won't get enough oxygen from the blood and it increases the risk of a blood clot forming.

4) Heart Attack

If a coronary artery becomes totally blocked (by a clot or atheroma), no blood is able to get through, which can cause a heart attack. The heart muscle is damaged because of the lack of oxygen. Heart attacks are also called myocardial infarctions.

Don't have a heart attack — try these questions instead:

1) What are cardiovascular diseases?
2) What are atheromas?
3) What causes a heart attack?

Answers

1) Diseases of the heart and blood vessels.
2) Fatty deposits that can build up in the walls of arteries.
3) A total block of a coronary artery.

Blood Vessels

Arteries, Arterioles, Capillaries and Veins

1) Arteries carry blood away from the heart.
2) They subdivide into smaller vessels called arterioles.
3) Arterioles subdivide into microscopic vessels called capillaries.
4) Capillaries join up to form veins.
5) Veins return blood to the heart.

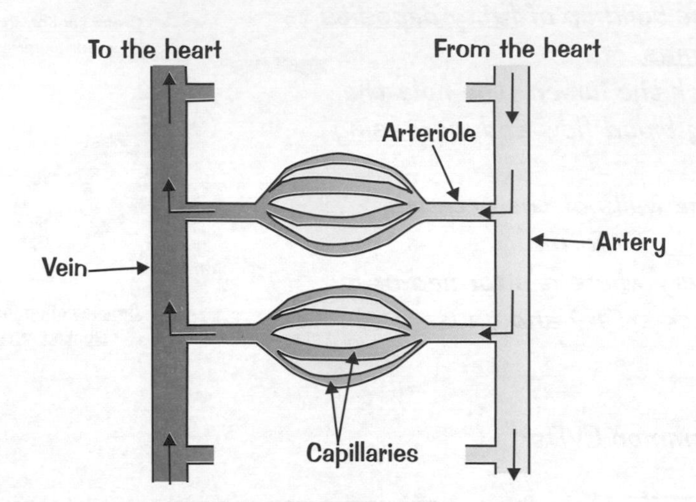

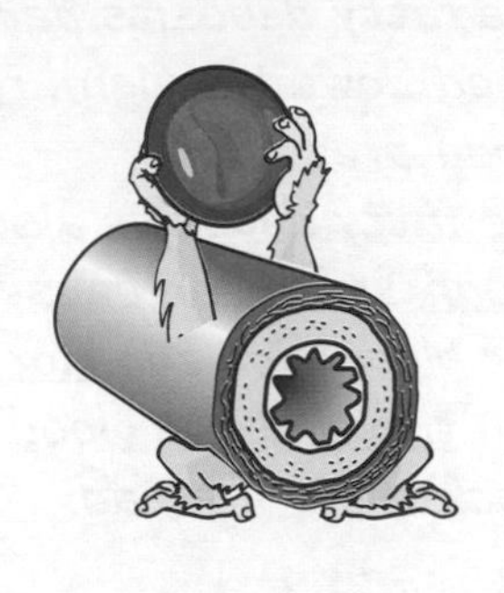

Arteries are Elastic

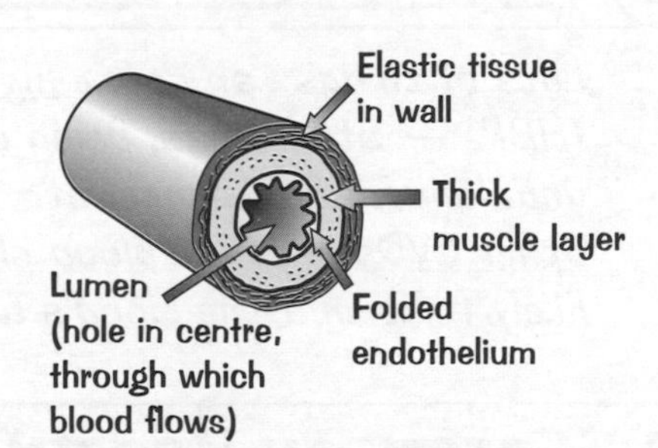

Arteries have a thick wall compared to the diameter of the lumen. There's an outer layer of fibrous tissue, then a thick layer of elastic tissue and smooth muscle, then a very thin inner layer of folded endothelial tissue.

When the ventricles contract, blood enters the arteries at high pressure. This stretches the folded endothelium and elastic walls. When the ventricles relax, it's the elastic recoil of the artery wall that keeps the blood pressure up. Important organs, like the kidneys, wouldn't be able to function if the blood pressure dropped too far between heartbeats.

Arterioles can Contract

Arterioles are narrower than arteries and they have a higher proportion of smooth muscle fibres and a lower proportion of elastic tissue.

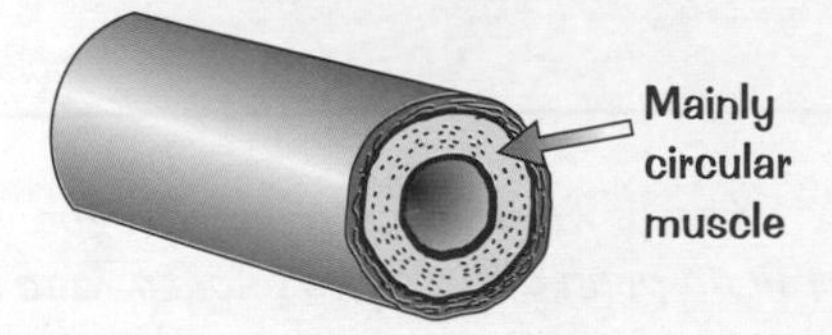

When the circular muscle fibres of an arteriole contract, the diameter of the lumen is reduced, so less blood flows through that vessel. Arterioles can control the amount of blood flowing to a particular organ.

Blood Vessels

Capillaries can Only be Seen With a Microscope

Capillary walls consist of a single layer of *endothelial cells* (cells that line the blood vessels). Some capillaries have *tiny gaps* between the endothelial cells.

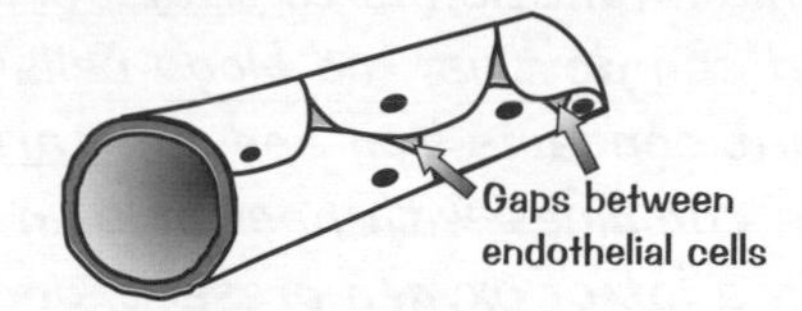

Capillaries are Well Suited to Their Job

1) The *very thin walls* and the *gaps* between the cells allow water and substances like glucose and oxygen to *diffuse quickly* from the blood into the cells. Waste products, such as carbon dioxide and urea, diffuse from the cells into the blood.
2) Organs contain thousands of capillaries, so altogether there's a *huge surface area* for the exchange of substances.
3) Blood flows quite *slowly* through capillaries. This allows *more time* for diffusion to occur.

Veins Have Valves

A vein has a *large lumen* and a relatively thin wall containing some elastic tissue and smooth muscle. Veins also have *valves* that prevent the blood flowing backwards.

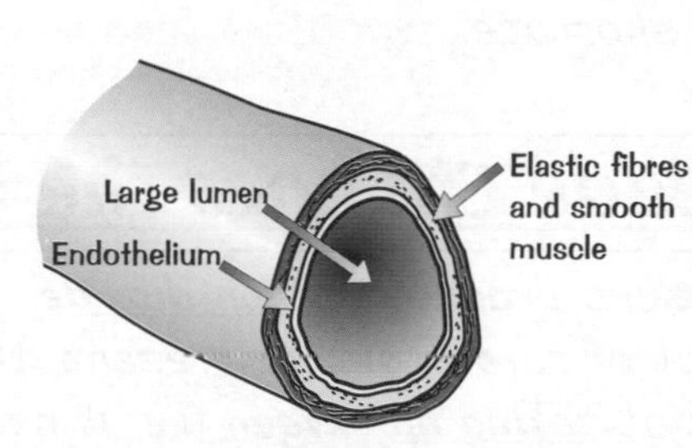

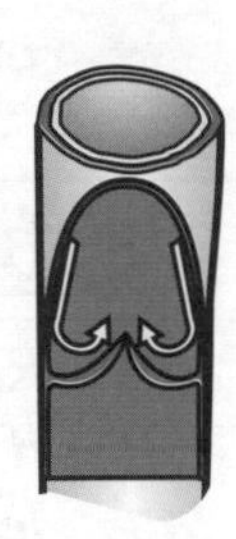

When the *leg muscles* contract they bulge and press on the walls of the veins, pushing the blood up the vein. When the muscles relax, the valves close. This action helps the blood *return* to the heart.

Have a go at the quick quiz below:

1) Explain the importance of the elastic tissue in the walls of arteries.
2) Describe how arterioles can control the amount of blood flowing to an organ.
3) Give three features of capillaries that maximise the exchange of substances between blood and cells.
4) Suggest why someone might faint if they stood absolutely still for a long time.

Answers

1) The elastic stretching and recoil of the artery walls prevents dramatic fluctuations in blood pressure that would damage important organs.
2) When the circular muscle fibres in the walls of arterioles contract they reduce the amount of blood flowing to the capillaries that they supply.
3) Very thin capillary walls. Many capillaries in each organ so there's a huge surface area. Blood flows relatively slowly through capillaries so there's more time for diffusion.
4) Leg muscles would not be contracting and relaxing so blood would not be helped back to the heart. Volume of blood in the heart would be less than usual and so the blood pressure in the arteries supplying the brain would decrease. This would result in insufficient oxygen and glucose reaching the brain cells.

Blood

Haemoglobin has Special Properties

1) The blood's main function is to transport materials to and from cells.
2) So the blood can do this, red blood cells are packed with haemoglobin, a protein that contains iron and can carry oxygen.
3) When oxygen combines with haemoglobin it forms oxyhaemoglobin.
4) When there's a lot of oxygen present, one molecule of haemoglobin can combine with four molecules of oxygen — the haemoglobin is '100% saturated'.
5) When less oxygen is present, fewer molecules of oxygen combine and the haemoglobin is less than 100% saturated.

It would be reasonable to expect that a graph of '% saturation of haemoglobin' against 'concentration of oxygen' would be a straight line (i.e. that the two would be proportional). However, when experiments are carried out and the results plotted, the line of best fit is S-shaped.

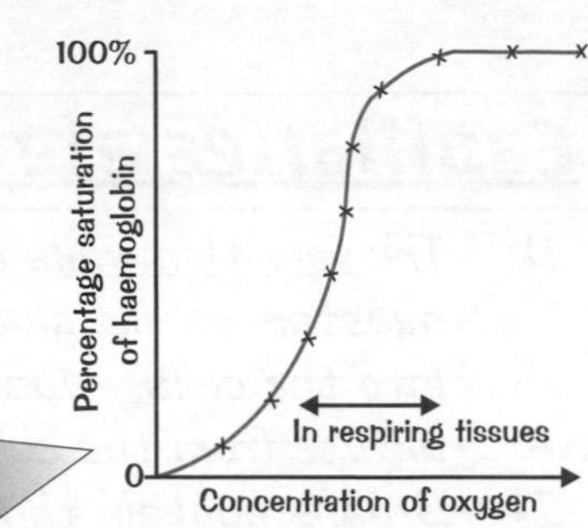

6) Haemoglobin has special properties that allow it to become fully saturated with oxygen in the capillaries around the alveoli of the lungs, where there's a high concentration of oxygen.
7) Then when it reaches respiring tissue, where there's less oxygen, it can give up almost all of its oxygen immediately — so the rate of respiration in the tissues isn't slowed down because of an oxygen shortage.

Carbon Dioxide Changes the Properties of Haemoglobin

1) Respiring tissues produce carbon dioxide.
2) If there's a lot of carbon dioxide present, the haemoglobin is less efficient at taking up oxygen (i.e. it needs to be exposed to a lot of oxygen before it becomes fully saturated).
3) But, when there's a lot of carbon dioxide present, the haemoglobin becomes more efficient at releasing oxygen (i.e. it can release more oxygen molecules in areas of fairly high oxygen demand).
4) This is good because it means that rapidly respiring tissues, e.g. contracting leg muscles and brain cells, get more oxygen.
5) This effect of carbon dioxide concentration on the oxygen-binding properties of haemoglobin is known as the Bohr effect.

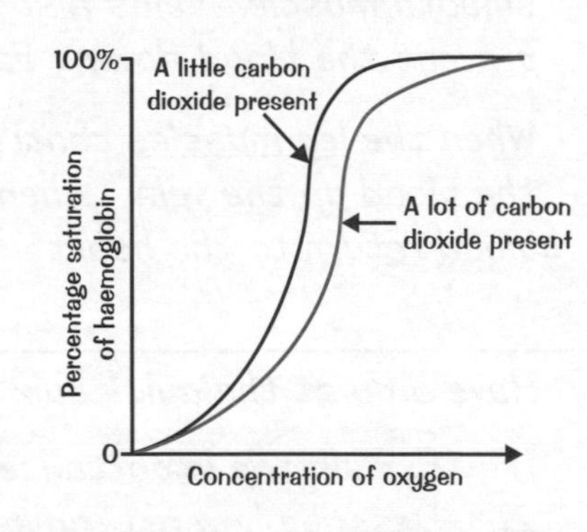

Understanding haemoglobin isn't easy — test yourself with these questions:

1) Name the substance picked up by the blood in the lungs.
2) How many molecules of oxygen are bound to a haemoglobin molecule when it's fully saturated?
3) Which gas affects the oxygen-binding properties of haemoglobin?
4) Under what circumstances does a tissue require the most oxygen?

Answers

1) Oxygen.
2) Four.
3) Carbon dioxide.
4) When it's rapidly respiring.

Variation and Evolution

We all Vary

1) All organisms are <u>different</u> from each other, e.g. giraffes are loads different from zebras, which are different from lions and tigers and bears...
2) Organisms of the <u>same species</u> also show <u>some variation</u>, e.g. humans show variation in height, weight, favourite colour of shoe polish...
3) Organisms of the <u>same species</u> are similar because they all have the <u>same genes</u> but they vary because they have <u>different versions</u> of those genes (called <u>alleles</u>). E.g. humans all have a gene for blood type, but they can have A, B or O alleles.

Variation Means Some Organisms are Better Adapted

An adaptation is a <u>characteristic</u> that helps an organism to <u>survive</u> and <u>have children</u>, e.g. polar bears have <u>thick</u>, <u>white fur</u> to stay warm and camouflaged in the snow. <u>Characteristics vary</u> in a population so some organisms are <u>better adapted</u> for certain conditions than others, e.g. polar bears with thicker fur are better adapted to survive in a cold environment than polar bears with thinner fur. The slightly different adaptations you get <u>within species</u> (e.g. slightly thicker fur on one polar bear compared to another) are coded for by <u>different alleles</u>.

Evolution

1) Evolution is the <u>gradual change</u> in the <u>characteristics</u> of a population from one generation to the next. The theory of evolution is that all organisms evolved from a <u>common ancestor</u> (organism) over <u>millions of years</u>.
2) There's <u>more than one</u> mechanism by which evolution occurs — the only one you need to know about is <u>natural selection</u>.

Natural Selection

1) Organisms from the <u>same population</u> all <u>vary</u> (e.g. different length of fur).
2) Organisms <u>compete</u> with each other for food, shelter, water etc.
3) Those with <u>better adaptations</u> (caused by different <u>alleles</u>) are more likely to find food, shelter, water etc, <u>survive</u> and have little <u>kiddies</u>. So they <u>pass on</u> their better adaptations (their alleles). E.g. bears with longer fur will stay warmer and be more likely to survive, and so have kids with longer fur.
4) Over time, the <u>number</u> of organisms with the better adaptations (alleles) <u>increases</u>.
5) The <u>whole population</u> of organisms <u>evolves</u> to have the better adaptations (alleles).

Check your understanding by having a go at these questions:

1) What is an allele?
2) What is an adaptation?
3) Briefly describe natural selection.

<u>Answers</u>

1) A different version of a gene.
2) Any feature that increases an organisms chance of survival.
3) Organisms with good adaptations (alleles) survive, have children and so pass on those good adaptations.

Classification

Classification Systems

1) *Classification is just sorting organisms into different groups and naming them.*
2) *It makes it easier for scientists to study organisms without getting confused, because every type of organism has a different name, e.g.* Homo sapien *(humans) or* Ursus maritimus *(polar bears).*
3) *Organisms are arranged into different groups depending on their similarities and differences, e.g. all animals are grouped together, and all plants are grouped together in a separate group because they're different to animals.*
4) *Organisms are placed in groups in classification hierarchies (pronounced: hire-arc-ees) — the biggest groups (e.g. animals, plants) are split into smaller groups (e.g. animals with a backbone in one group and animals without a backbone in another). These groups are split again into more smaller groups, and so on.*

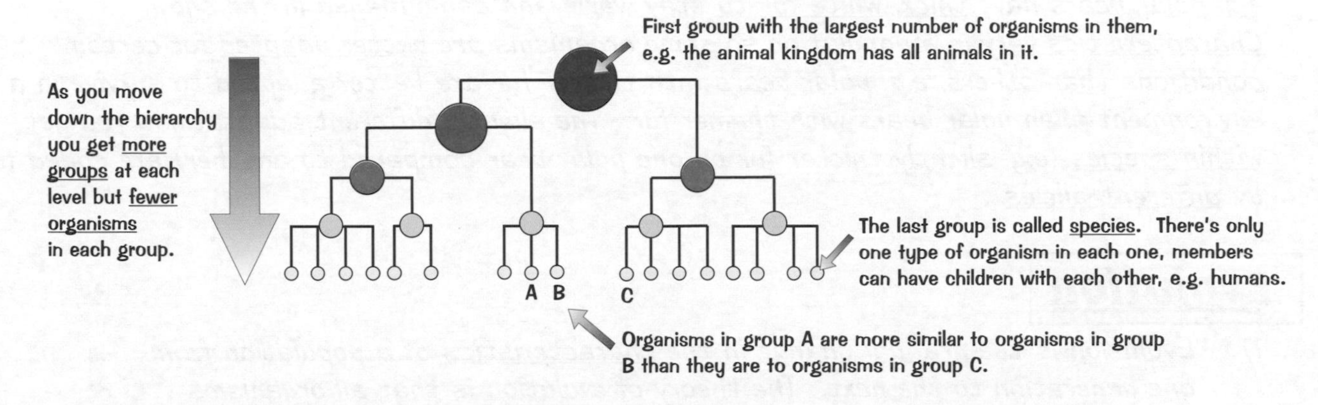

A species is a group of organisms that look similar and can reproduce to give fertile offspring (their children can also reproduce).

Classification Systems are Based on Lots of Things

1) *Older classification systems grouped organisms based only on how they look, e.g. four limbs, six eyes, bum chin...*
2) *Newer systems use looks and lots of other things:*
   - *DNA — how similar and different the base sequence is (e.g. ATTTAC vs. ATTTAT).*
   - *Other molecules — e.g. immune system cells, proteins and enzymes.*
   - *Early development — how they grow from an embryo to a baby.*

Another mini quiz to get your teeth into:

1) *What does classification involve?*
2) *What is a species?*
3) *List four things newer classification systems use to group organisms.*

Answers

1) *Sorting organisms into groups based on their similarities and differences, and naming them.*
2) *A group of organisms that look similar and can reproduce to give fertile offspring.*
3) *How they look, DNA, other molecules and early development.*

Xylem and Phloem

Xylem Tissue Transports Water and Minerals from Roots

Water from the soil enters the roots by osmosis. Then it travels through the root to the xylem — the tissue that transports water through the plant and up to the leaves.
Water can travel through the roots in two ways:

The symplast system:

- Some water moves through the root via the cytoplasm of the root cells. The water has to cross the cell membrane, which regulates the passage of the water and dissolved minerals.

The apoplast system:

- The water moves through the cell walls and the spaces between the cells.
- There are no membranes to regulate the passage.

Water Travels Up the Plant Through the Xylem Tissue

The cells that make up the tubes (vessels) of xylem tissue are dead, waterproof and hollow. This means water can move through them easily. Water is pulled up through the xylem tissue by a combination of factors: cohesion, tension and adhesion:

1) Water evaporates from inside the leaf leaving a higher concentration of solutes.
2) Water from the nearest xylem vessel enters by osmosis.
3) Water molecules stick together because of weak hydrogen bonds between them — this is called cohesion.
4) As water molecules leave the xylem vessel they pull up further molecules, so the whole column of water is pulled up.
5) Evaporation pulls the water column upwards and gravity pulls it down, so the water column is under tension.
6) The adhesion of water molecules to the sides of the xylem vessels stops the column breaking.

Phloem Transports Organic Compounds

Sugars and other organic compounds are transported through plants in phloem tissue. Phloem tissue is also arranged in tubes so the solutions of sugar etc can move through them easily.

1) The movement of carbohydrates and other organic compounds in plants is known as translocation.
2) It occurs in the sieve tubes of the phloem tissue.
3) Companion cells next to the sieve tubes are believed to actively transport sugar into the sieve tubes, and then water follows by osmosis.

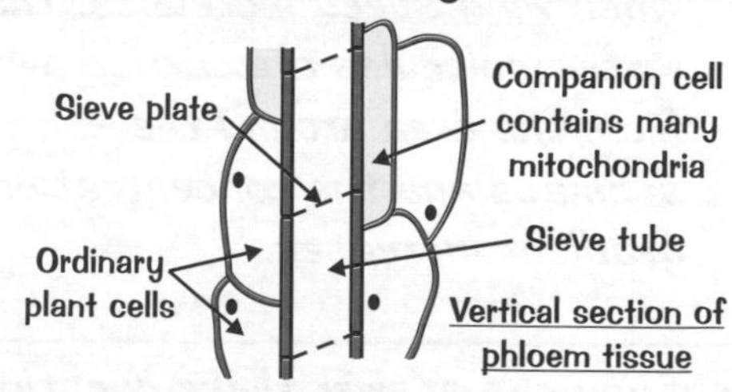

Have a go at these questions:

1) In the symplast system, which part of the cell does water move through?
2) Why is the column of water in the xylem under tension?
3) Why do companion cells contain many mitochondria?

Answers

1) Cytoplasm.
2) Transpiration is pulling the water up and gravity is pulling it down.
3) For respiration to release energy for active transport of sugar.

Transpiration

Transpiration is the Evaporation of Water from Plants

Evaporation from the leaves and stems of plants is called *transpiration*. It has *two* main effects:

1) It *transports* water and minerals.
2) It *cools* the plant.

If the rate of transpiration is greater than the rate of water uptake by the roots, the plant wilts.

Plants can't avoid transpiration, even if they need to — it happens because they need to exchange gases for *photosynthesis*.

Water is Lost Because of Gas Exchange

1) The *waxy cuticle* that covers stems and leaves reduces water loss but it's impermeable to *carbon dioxide*, which is needed for photosynthesis.
2) *Stomata* (singular — '*stoma*') are *holes* in the leaves of plants that can be opened, letting *carbon dioxide in* and *oxygen and water out*.
3) Most plants only open their stomata when the light intensity is high enough for a good *rate of photosynthesis*. When they do open them *water* diffuses *out*.

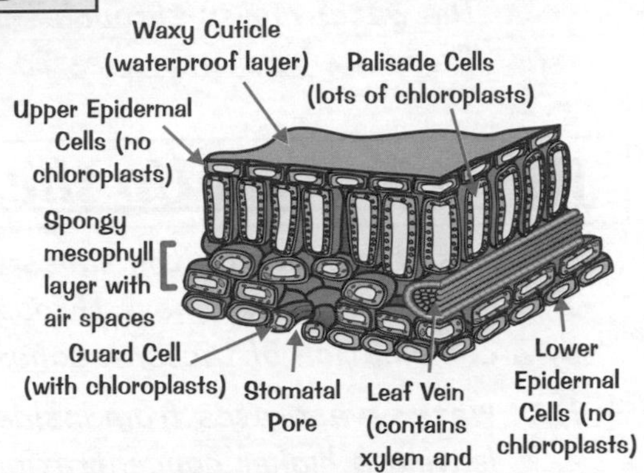

Certain Factors Increase the Rate of Transpiration

Water molecules generally diffuse from a region of *higher water concentration* to a region of *lower water concentration*. The *bigger* the difference in concentration, the *faster* the movement.

1) Air inside a leaf is always saturated with water, so any decrease in *humidity* outside the leaf will increase the rate of transpiration.
2) An increase in *temperature* increases the evaporation rate of the water. It also increases the amount of water vapour that the air can contain. This maintains a concentration gradient.
3) When *wind speed* increases, the water molecules are carried away from the area around the stomata and the concentration gradient increases.

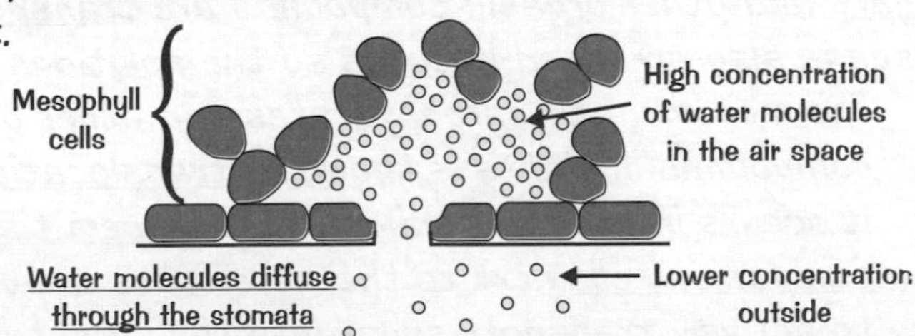

See if you can answer these questions:

1) What is transpiration?
2) Suggest how transpiration might help a plant to survive in a hot climate.
3) Why do plants need stomata?
4) Name three conditions that increase the rate of transpiration.

Answers

1) The evaporation of water from the leaves and stems of plants.
2) Transpiration cools the plant.
3) To allow carbon dioxide to diffuse into the plant for photosynthesis, and to allow oxygen and water out.
4) Decreased humidity, increased temperature and increased wind speed.

Reliability and Validity

Evidence is Reliable If It Can be Repeated

Scientific evidence needs to be reliable (or reproducible). If it isn't, then it doesn't really help you. When you're doing an investigation, you need to repeat your experiment several times to make sure your results are reliable — you should get round about the same answer each time.

RELIABLE means the results can be consistently reproduced in independent experiments.

Example

In 1998, some scientists claimed that there was a link between the MMR vaccine and autism. It was big news — if true, it would have meant that all MMR vaccinations would have to be stopped. But other scientists just couldn't get the same results — they weren't reliable. Since then other scientists have shown that there's no link between MMR and autism.

Evidence Also Needs to be Valid and Representative

Collecting reliable data is important, but if the data doesn't answer your original question, it won't be any use. You need to think about what data to collect to make sure your results will be valid.

VALID means that the data is reliable AND answers the original question.

It's also important that you base your data on a big enough sample. The danger with a small sample is that your data might only be true for that sample — you won't be able to extend your results to other situations because they aren't representative of the whole population.

Controlling All the Variables is Really Hard

The difficulty with a lot of scientific investigations is that it's very hard to control all the variables that might (just might) be having an effect.

Example

Studies have shown a correlation between the variables "presence of power lines" and "incidence of cancer". But this doesn't prove that power lines cause cancer — other explanations are possible. For example, power lines are often near busy roads, so it might be that living in an area of high pollution increases the incidence of cancer and that the power lines have no effect.

In the lab it's different — scientists can control the variables so that the only one that changes is the one they're investigating — all the others are kept constant. In experiments like this, you can say that one variable causes the other one to change because you have made sure that nothing else could be causing the change.

You Don't Need to Lie to Make Things Biased

When you write up your results, it's important to give a balanced view of the data so that the reader can make up their own mind about it. People who want to make a point can sometimes present data in a biased way to suit their own purposes — e.g. by only using the bits of data that support their argument, or by phrasing things in a leading way.

Graphs and Relationships

Repeating an Experiment Lets You Find a Mean Result

If you repeat an experiment, your results will usually be slightly different each time you do it. You can use the mean (or average) of the measurements to represent all the values. The more times you repeat the experiment the more reliable the average will be. To find the mean:

ADD TOGETHER all the data values then DIVIDE by the total number of values in the sample.

Graphs Are Used to Show Relationships

Once you've collected all your data and worked out the mean results, you need to analyse it to find any relationships between the variables. The easiest way to do this is to draw a graph, then describe what you see.

Example

Jamie did an experiment to see how the rate of an enzyme-controlled reaction changed depending on the temperature. He carried out an enzyme-controlled reaction at 9 different temperatures. For each temperature he measured the rate of reaction. Jamie has drawn a graph to see if the two variables are related. He has included a line of best fit, which shows the correlation between rate of reaction and temperature.

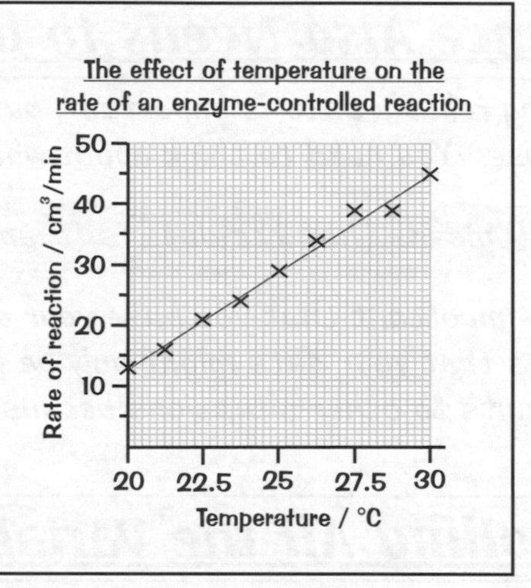

Drawing Graphs is Easy — When You Know How

Graphs are really useful for showing whether variables are related, so make sure you know how to draw them.

1) *Get your axes the right way round — the thing you change (the independent variable) goes on the x-axis. The thing you measure (the dependent variable) goes on the y-axis.*

y-axis
x-axis

2) *Think about the scale to use on each axis. You should make the most of the space you have by spreading the points out so that you can see what's going on.*

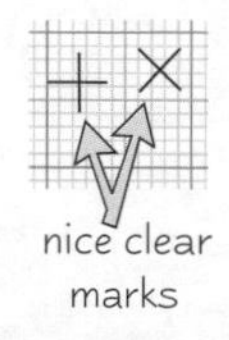

3) *Plot the data points — use a sharp pencil and make a neat little cross.*

4) *Give your graph a title so it's clear what it's about.*

5) *Draw a line of best fit through your data. Try to draw the line through or as near to as many points as possible, ignoring anomalous results. Don't just connect up your data points — the line of best fit is meant to show the general trend in the data points, not their exact locations.*

Correlation and Cause

Lines of Best Fit Are Used to Show Trends...

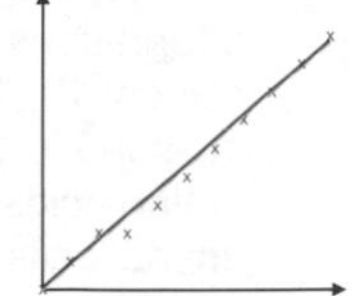

The line of best fit on Jamie's graph shows that as the temperature of the reaction is increased, the rate of reaction also increases. This is called a positive correlation. The data points are all quite close to the line of best fit, so you can say the correlation is strong. If they were more spread out, the correlation would be weak.

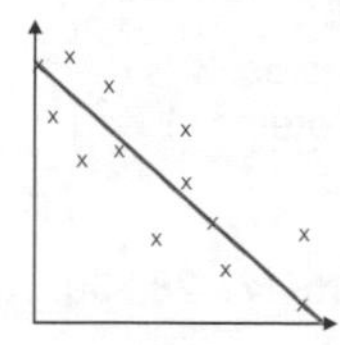

Variables can also be negatively correlated — this means one variable increases as the other one decreases. Look at the way the line of best fit slopes to work out what sort of correlation your graph shows.

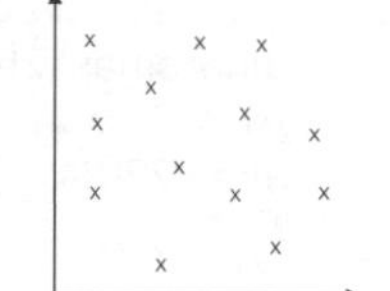

Sometimes the graph won't show any clear trend and you won't be able to draw a line of best fit. In this case, you say there's no correlation between the variables.

...and Estimate Values Between Data Points

When you do an experiment it's impossible to measure every data point. Instead, you can use the line of best fit to estimate values in between the data points that you actually measured — this is called interpolation. Or, you can use it to estimate values outside the range you measured — this is extrapolation. The method is the same for both — you draw a line from one axis to the line of best fit, then turn and go straight to the other axis and read off the value you end up at.

The estimates you get from interpolation are usually fairly trustworthy — if you've measured a series of points that show a clear trend, it's unlikely that anything weird will happen between them. Extrapolation can be a bit dodgy because it assumes your trend will continue in the same way. Take Jamie's graph — extrapolation predicts that a temperature around 32.5 °C would produce a rate of reaction of about 50 cm^3/min. It might, but then again it might not — you can't rely on the result.

Correlation Doesn't Always Mean Cause

Be careful what you conclude from an experiment — just because two variables are correlated, it doesn't necessarily mean that one causes the other.

In lab-based experiments like Jamie's, you can say that the independent variable causes the dependent variable to change — the increase in temperature causes an increase in the rate of the reaction. You can say this because everything else has stayed the same — nothing else could be causing the change.

Outside a lab, it can be much harder:

> Example
>
> Kate measured the level of air pollution and the incidence of TB, to see whether the two are related. Her results show a positive correlation between the variables — where the level of pollution is highest, the incidence of TB is also highest.

From Kate's results, you can't say that air pollution causes TB.
Neither can you say that TB causes air pollution.
It could be either way round... or one change might not cause the other at all — you just can't tell.

Index